SILENT EVIDENCE

Firearms (Forensic Ballistics) and Toolmarks

Cases from Forensic Science

To Lambert Wood —

Good reading + long life,

Charles Meyers

by
Charles Meyers

2004
Parkway Publishers, Inc.
Boone, North Carolina

Library of Congress Cataloging-in-Pubication Data

Meyers, Charles, 1926-
    Silent evidence : firearms (forensic ballistics) and toolmarks : cases from
    forensic science / by Charles Meyers.

    p. cm.
Includes bibliographical references.
    ISBN 1-887905-39-1
    1. Forensic ballistics--United States. 2. Murder--United States. I. Title.
HV8077.M49 2004
363.25'62--dc22

                                                        2004019579

Typeset and Cover Design by: Beth Jacquot

    Portions of this book originally appeared in the following publications:
"Interesting Applications of Tool Mark Identification," *Journal of Forensic
Sciences* vol. 6(no. 3) (July 1961) 316-320; "The Mythical Striation Match,"
Association of Firearms and Toolmark Examiners (AFTE) Journal, vol.
24(no. 4) (October 1992) 364-365; and "Firearms and Toolmark Identification
– An Introduction," *Association of Firearms and Toolmark Examiners (AFTE)
Journal*, vol. 25(no. 4) (October 1993) 281-285.

DEDICATION

"This is humbly dedicated to my family; my children — Robin, Kathy, Kim, Kurt, and Kelly, and my devoted wife Nancy, all of whom have endured my "war stories" for so long."

"Wherever he (the criminal) steps, whatever he touches — even unconsciously — will serve as silent evidence against him. Not only his fingerprints and his shoeprints, but also his hair, the fibers from his clothes, the glass he breaks, the tool marks he leaves, the paint he scratches, the blood or semen that he deposits or collects — all these and more — bear mute evidence against him. This is evidence that does not forget. It is not confused by the excitement of the moment. It is not absent because human witnesses are. It is factual evidence. Physical evidence cannot be wrong; it cannot perjure itself; it cannot be totally absent. Only in its interpretation can there be error."

(Harris v. United States, 331US145, 1947)
"Crime Investigation," 2nd Edition
Authored by Paul L. Kirk
Edited by John I. Thornton
Published by John Wiley & Sons, 1974
New York

PREFACE

This collection of cases highlights the influence of Crime Scene evidence in the forensic discipline of Firearms and Toolmark Identification. The collection illustrates the imaginative work of crime scene investigators, criminal investigators, and crime laboratory analysts. These cases may be of interest to students of forensic science, criminal justice, criminal law, and the general public.

An addendum, "A Primer on Firearms and Toolmark Identification", is included for those readers who desire a deeper understanding of the discipline and its scientific foundation.

This book, for the most part, attempts to let the evidence speak for itself. Criminal investigations may be colored by alleged motives, criminal history, witness exaggerations and confusion, and even greed. However, the analyst must keep an open mind, approach the physical evidence from a strictly professional standpoint, and not be swayed by investigative pressure. In the majority of cases, analysts are not aware of much of the investigative information unless it directly impinges on the evidence they are about to examine.

Over the years, analysts have, of necessity, become more specialized. Increased caseloads, expanding technology, and judicial restraints on expert testimony demand more education and specialized training. As one writer humorously but somewhat accurately put it, "an expert is someone who knows more and more about less and less." The TV image of certain "experts" as individuals who know everything there is to know about everything is misleading to say the least.

Although, many of the cases involve horrific crimes, the emphasis is on the manner of solution and the courtroom proofs, not on the gory aspects of the crime itself. These tales are from actual cases in which the author was involved. As the old saying goes, "the stories are true, only the names have been changed to protect the innocent."

CONTENTS

KEYWORD DEFINITIONS

Criminalist: One who by virtue of his/her education and training is considered to be acceptably competent to practice criminalistics.

Criminalistics: The application of the instruments and methods of physical science to the detection and solution of crime.

Firearms & Toolmark

Identification: That discipline of the Forensic Sciences directed to the examination and comparative analysis of firearms and ammunition components, and other tools and markings they produce.

Forensic Science: Scientific knowledge applied to the purposes of the law and the courts.

Identification: Individualization; Causal Identity (i.e., questioned and known markings resulting from the same source, e.g., fatal and test bullet fired through the same barrel).

The Scientist: "Their business is not with the possible but the actual…with a world that is. They have but one desire—to know the truth. They have but one fear—to believe a lie."

John Tyndall

*Fig. 1—Bullet comparison microscopes—top circa 1930s;
bottom circa 1980s

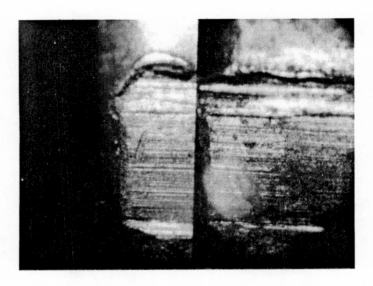

*Fig. 2—"Textbook bullet match"—photomicrograph through
1930s microscope; evidence bullet left of line, test right.

*Fig. 3 —"Textbook toolmark match"—through 1980s microscope;
evidence markings left, test markings right of dividing line.

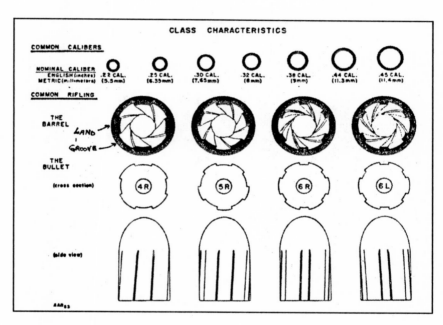

*Fig. 4—Bullet/rifling class characteristics (courtesy of A. Biasotti)

THE TEEN-AGE SNIPER

I

The Teen Connection

It was early winter in Southern Michigan and evening traffic was extremely light throughout the suburban residential district. As the late afternoon light faded, a faint "crack" was heard in the neighborhood. An experienced shooter or small game hunter may have recognized the sound as that of a small caliber firearm. In the center of one block, a noticeable hole surrounded by radiating cracks, had appeared in the picture window of a beautiful home. The occupants, having heard a peculiar noise, discovered this hole and damage to a buffet across the dining room. Nearby, they found a misshapen hunk of lead displaying a surface with minute embedded slivers and white powdered glass. At this point, the occupants called the Township Police.

A patrol officer responded, checked the damage, prepared a report, and took charge of the metal object. Within a few days, the evidence was turned over to the Identification Officer from the Sheriff's Office, who had some experience with firearms and crime scenes. After a brief examination of the object, the Deputy confirmed that it was a badly mutilated .22 caliber lead bullet. A check of the neighborhood revealed no one who had seen anything amiss. This shooting, in a real sense, was not a major crime. Vandalism or malicious destruction of property is all too common, even in nice neighborhoods.

About a week later, a similar incident was reported in the same community, and only a few blocks away from the first. In a matter of days, officers were investigating a third report, again where a window was severely damaged and .22 caliber bullet fragments were discovered. By now the community was alarmed, and the Township Police recognized an apparent pattern that was no coincidence. The local newspaper was now showing more than passing interest in the incidents.

An extensive neighborhood search for witnesses and/or evidence was conducted. Again, no one reported seeing anything unusual or anyone related to the incident. There was a light snowfall prior to this latest shooting and officers discovered partial shoeprints, in the alleyway nearby, alongside a fired .22 caliber cartridge case. The prints were of a small size made by sneaker or tennis shoe. The investigators speculated that a teen-age boy might have fired the shot from this location.

The local newspaper carried the story and passed it on to the neighboring large city press. There may have been a news shortage at the time as the City Press carried the story on the front page as the "Teen Age Sniper Shooting".

During the next couple of weeks, there were two more such incidents, all in the same community and all involving windows shot out. The press reported each new case as "Teen Age Sniper Strikes Again". By now, the entire Township was well aware of the situation, and it was a prime topic for their conversations. The police were primarily concerned, that should the problem continue, someone might get hurt.

The Crime

One cold Sunday, snow had fallen much of the day. Late in the afternoon, what the officers feared came to pass. In the McPherson home, the family members were gathered in the lower level family room. Scott McPherson, the 16 year old son, finished a game of chess with his father, Neil. Nancy, the 14 year old daughter excused herself to go up to her room to gather schoolbooks for homework. Betty McPherson, the mother, announced she was going up to the kitchen to prepare lunch and fresh coffee. Scott took leave to go up to his room to finish a school project. Neil retrieved a partly finished book and started to read where he had left off.

After about 30 minutes with no call from Betty to "come and get it", Neil decided to see how she was coming along. As he entered the kitchen, he was surprised to note water running in the sink and shocked to see Betty lying on the floor unconscious. After a hasty attempt to revive her, the paramedics were called. Betty was placed on a stretcher and rushed to the nearest hospital. Shortly thereafter, she was pronounced DOA (dead on arrival).

Neil first learned that early diagnosis indicated sudden incapacitation and death, possibly from a brain aneurysm. Later, x-rays showed a small very dense object inside her cranial cavity, with an associated "snowstorm" of microscopic dense particulate. The hospital radiologist had seen similar radiographs before and recognized the damage from a small caliber bullet.

The County Coroner and Pathologist agreed to an immediate autopsy and one was conducted that night. As expected, the cause of death was a severely damaged .22 caliber lead bullet. Upon removal from Betty McPherson's brain, the bullet was partly cleaned and in addition to human matter, traces of foreign material were found embedded in the bullet's damaged sides. This debris was identified as microscopic particles of crushed and powered glass.

Initially, no bullet entry wound had been observed. Now the pathologist could trace the .22 caliber bullet pathway from entrance in the corner of the eye, at about the tear duct, through the eye orbit and upwards into the brain.

It was time for the police to determine what had happened. Back at the McPherson home they quickly discovered a hole through the kitchen window's storm glass with a larger, more irregular, hole through the inner pane. This effect apparently due to the bullet "mushrooming" as it entered. Soft lead and hollow-point bullets tend to expand back onto their sides when they strike hard objects, thereby creating a mushroom shaped effect. The window was covered with sheer curtains which also demonstrated apparent bullet perforation. The coffee pot was lying in the bottom of the sink. It appeared that Mrs. McPherson was attempting to fill the pot with water when the bullet crashed through the window.

Investigators checked out-of-doors and in nearby fresh snow for any evidence of the shooter. Alongside a garage across the street, they found several partial small sneaker prints in the snow. They then attempted to visually line-up the center of the window bullet holes, the hole through the curtain, and the possible shooter position next to the garage. This line-up seemed to be in agreement. Once this was accomplished, they placed an officer in the kitchen, approximately in alignment with the probable bullet pathway. This was done in the late afternoon with approximately the same lighting condition. A second officer, placed alongside the garage at the likely shooter position, could not see the officer in the kitchen. Apparently, the teen-age sniper had made a tragic mistake. That's how the press reported it!

III

The Crime Scene Check and the Solution

The following day, two officers from the State Crime Laboratory were testifying in Circuit Court in the neighboring city. As they left the courtroom, they were approached by a good friend of theirs, an Identification Officer with the Sheriff's Office. He asked if they were aware of the "sniper" case and described the death that had just occurred. He stated further that he was not satisfied with the investigation at this point and asked if they would go to the scene with him and look it over. They, of course, readily agreed.

A careful examination of the bullet holes indicated that the Deputy's suspicions were correct. The outer hole was somewhat irregular and missing some glass from the margins. The inner window hole was enlarged, more irregular and missing glass from most of the margins. However, the analysts were able to find a portion of the original outline of the entrance hole and thereby create a more accurate flight-path which indicated entry at a significant angle rather than nearly parallel to the ground.

In some cases, it is necessary to determine the direction of bullet flight where shots are fired through a hard smooth surface such as plastic, glass, or bone. There are several basic factors that assist in this regard. On the entry side, the surface is smooth in appearance and feel, up to the very margins of the hole. If not readily visible, this can be felt with the fingertips. On the exit side, the material is cratered, rough and irregular with the hole enlarged. Again, this feature can be visualized or felt. However, it must be remembered that the material can be fragmented and broken away from the original outline and thereby create confusion in regard to the bullet's actual path. The investigators must find at the entrance hole at least a portion of the original symmetrical outline and smooth surface. Here, misalignment of the bullet's path caused confusion at the very outset.

Correct alignment produced a completely different picture. A backwards projection from the window followed a path angling downwards along an imaginary line that ended in the center of the victim's front yard! This meant the barrel of the firearm was held along this line when the fatal shot was fired. (See Figs. 5-8).

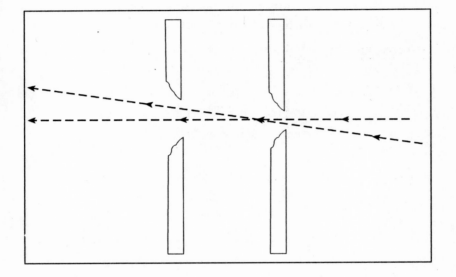

*Fig. 5 – Projected bullet pathways

*Fig. 6 – Windows through which bullet passed.

*Fig. 7 – Metal rod indicates true bullet path.

*Fig. 8 – Bullet path projected from end point in front yard

The yard was covered with snow and there were no footwear prints or impressions to be seen. The only cleared area was on the sidewalk directly in front of the kitchen window. Further examination disclosed traces of what appeared as specks of "black pepper" on the glass and the sill underneath. It was now obvious that the shooter could not help but see the victim and was standing within a few feet of the window when the shot was fired.

When a firearm is discharged, the products of combustion are forced out of the barrel along with the bullet. Much of this debris consists of partially burned gunpowder particles. These small granules are light in weight and have poor ballistic properties. Therefore, they only fly for several feet before they are spent and fall to the ground. Their presence indicated the shot was fired from only a few feet away from the window. Laboratory examination confirmed the lifted particles were in fact granules of smokeless gunpowder. It was now very clear that this was not vandalism. This was murder!

After a brief investigation, the crime was solved. The solution was a bizarre as the crime itself. Detectives zeroed in on the murdered woman's son. They learned that he had a grudge against his mother. She was a strict disciplinarian and Scott felt smothered. They also learned that a companion of his was in trouble with the law. They picked up the friend for a friendly discussion. He told them that he and Scott had broken into a small business and Scott retained a .22 caliber pistol they removed from the store.

It was now time for an interview with Scott. To the officers' surprise, he readily admitted to the stolen pistol and that he was the sniper. Further, he admitted he shot out windows to set the stage for killing his mother when the time was ripe. He reportedly assumed the incident might be passed off as a senseless tragedy, caused by an unknown "Teen-Age Sniper"!

THE UNSOLVED FAMILY MURDERS

You Be The Jury

INTRODUCTION

In over fifty years of experience in assisting with the investigation of murder and the resulting courtroom proofs, this case was the most heinous, mystifying, and mind-boggling of the author's career.

THE PROLOGUE

It was summer, a beautiful day, and school was out. In the Northern part of the State, many of the cottages and lodges were now occupied by busy families. In this secluded area, near the sandy lakeshore, the gentle breezes stirred the tops of the tall oaks and pines. The idyllic day was being spoiled by a brisk breeze and the horrible message it carried. One lodge happened to be downwind at this time.

The message was transmitted to the Stewart family, who had been in and out during the day. There had been prior hints of the same problem, for some time. But now, the problem, a very disagreeable odor, was even more powerful, suggesting the possible death and decay of some sort of animal. The odor seemed to emanate from a distant neighbors' lodge. The Stewarts theorized some animal may have crawled under the porch of the neighboring lodge and died there.

The Stewarts knew that their neighbors, the Gooden family, had planned on leaving for an extended trip, nearly a month before. They had mentioned they were planning to visit several states, including Kentucky and Tennessee.

They noticed that the two Gooden family cars were still parked in the driveway of the beautiful log and stone lodge. They knew the Goodens were planning on flying out on their trip and thought they had hired someone to take them to the local airport.

However, it was past time to attend to the nasty odor problem and they placed a call to Eino Maki, who lived a few miles away and provided caretaker and maintenance service to a number of lodges in this area. He promised he would drop by and check it out.

I

The Crime Scene

The lodge was located at the end of a trail-road drive, about one-half mile off the main highway and nearly concealed by a thick wooded area. It was one of a number of expensive "cottages" on large plots in this small community on the lakeshore. The owners of the area lodges were all considered "well-to-do". This particular building consisted of six rooms on two floors, with an exterior of log and stone. The original developers were part of the Maki family and Eino Maki knew this lodge very well.

Maki, along with his friend and helper, Charlie the Indian, responded to the report of the odor problem. Although no trace of a dead animal could be seen from the exterior, they couldn't help but notice the powerful and disagreeable smell that seemed to come from inside. As the two men circled the lodge, they observed a note taped to one pane of a sectional window. The note explained the family would be gone on an extended trip. A check of the doors revealed they were both locked and secure. A peek through window glass showed nothing apparently amiss.

Eino decided to investigate further and obtained tools from a nearby shed. One door was forced open and he peeked inside. Through the hum of blow flies and the blue-gray smoke-like haze hanging the air, he could make out the shape of a human body, partly covered, on the living room floor. Charlie and he ran to the closest occupied cabin and placed a call to the County Sheriff's Office. Thus began one of the State's most repulsive, complex, and frustrating murder cases.

The Under-sheriff and other deputies responded quickly to the call. After a preliminary examination of the lodge and its contents, calls were placed to the Coroner's Office and to the State Police asking for assistance. The call was received in the early evening and the State Police Crime Laboratory crew arrived later that night.

When the crime lab crew arrived at the scene, they were briefed on the crime discovery. The Under-sheriff assured them that the scene had been protected and no evidence had been disturbed. The crime scene team included officers with extensive crime scene and latent fingerprint experience. They were assisted by a member of the Department of Health's Crime Detection Laboratory staff. The team was headed by Sgt. Paul Brandeis of the Latent Print Unit, and ably assisted by Officer Herb Olmstead. These two had achieved a reputation as two of the finest crime scene investigators and laboratory specialists in the State. They were accompanied by Officers Hugh Pike, David Largent, and Lewis Woolsy. All were considered to be knowledgeable and conscientious crime scene investigators. The officers began a methodical and painstaking investigation that lasted for several days, involving a search of the home and premises and the autopsies.

A pole lamp in the backyard and a dormer light on the side of the cottage were illuminated. The yard displayed a number of large maple trees and evergreen shrubs on two sides. Two late model cars were parked on the side of the building. They were both locked. The condition of cars and driveway indicated they had been locked and parked in these positions for some time. Any tire impressions that may have been in the driveway had been washed away by recent rains.

The lodge was 1 ½ stories, with a stone foundation, and log siding. The front of the cottage faced the lake. The two entrance doors were on opposite ends of the living/dining area. The living room portion was bisected by a large stone fireplace. The window near the rear entrance door consisted of two rows of small vertical panes. Taped to the window was a paper napkin displaying a note stating "Be back by 7-10, Gooden". Above this note was a separately printed note on a slip of paper with the message "We were here, The Stoigers". Removal of the napkin note from the window revealed four small caliber entrance bullet holes perforating the glass pane. A search of the grounds nearby disclosed four .22 caliber rim-fire Remington fired cartridge cases (shells), all in a nearly straight row along the side of the building. The investigators soon learned the crimes and areas of interest involved the ground floor of the lodge. This floor embraced the living/dining area, a separate kitchen, large bathroom and two sizeable bedrooms. There was a central hall that provided access to the bathroom and bedrooms. The building was heated by a floor furnace, with a large register in the middle of the hallway. A stairwell in one corner of the living area led to an upstairs bedroom.

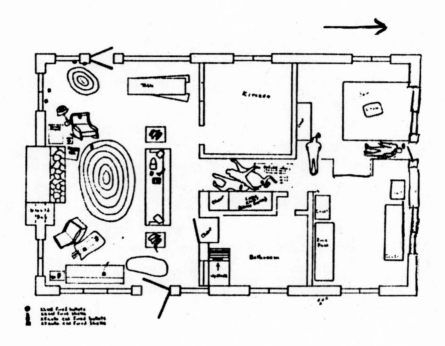

*Fig. 9 – Original Rough Crime Scene sketch

The living area displayed the typical furniture; two couches, a stuffed chair and rocker, end tables, a rustic style wood table with two benches and a large oval braided rug centered between the furniture cluster.

One couch was partly covered with three light coats, a man's, a woman's, and a small child's. There were three camera cases placed on the floor near this couch and the rear door.

The wooden table displayed partial decks of cards, arranged to indicate that two persons had been playing solitaire.

The first victim was lying on a section of the living room floor. It was that of a 40 year old woman, later identified as Mrs. Sherry Gooden, wife and mother of the other victims. Her body was face down on the floor and she had been covered with a blanket over her upper body and down to her knees. Her clothing was in disarray and the officers felt they were arranged in such a fashion to create the illusion that she had been raped.

The second victim, Richard Gooden, husband and father, was lying face down on top of the hot-air register of the floor furnace, in about the center of the hallway.

The youngest son, Mark Gooden, age 12, was lying face down on top of his father's body. A throw rug had been placed over Mark's body, extending from his shoulders down to his upper legs.

A fourth victim, Sarah Gooden, youngest child, was lying in the hallway, face up, next to the body of her brother, Mark.

Next, the body of Robert Gooden, age 19, the oldest son, was lying face down with his upper body over the threshold of the master bedroom door and with his lower extremities into the hallway.

The sixth and last victim, Greg Gooden, age 16, was inside the master bedroom, lying on his back.

It was theorized that the older boys had been playing solitaire at the time of the fatal assault and they may have attempted to gain access to a .22 caliber rifle and supply of ammunition located in the master bedroom closet in order to defend the family.

Packed luggage on the bed indicated that the victims were ready to leave on the announced trip, before their plans were abruptly changed.

There were bloody drag marks on the wooden floor indicating movement of some of the bodies. It was believed that the killer(s) placed them in a manner so that anyone peering through the windows would not be able to see them.

One set of bloody footwear impressions was located on the flooring, indicating the possible involvement of only one killer. However, the number of victims and the circumstances surrounding the scene are the factors that often lead police to conjecture, more than one person must be involved. This type of thinking, during many phases of this investigation, worked against the lead investigators and seemed to contradict the evidence. This theory still exists among some officers who had a degree of involvement in the case. And yet, there are many recorded cases illustrating this theory is often wrong; e.g., the Richard Specht case in Chicago, Danny Rollings in Florida, and the "boy next door" Ted Bundy, to cite just a few.

A search of the living room area revealed the presence of five (5) .25 auto. caliber fired cartridge cases, two (2) .25 auto. caliber fired jacketed bullets, and three (3) .22 long rifle caliber fired lead bullets. The three .22 caliber bullets were removed from the stuffed rocker and the frame near the front door and adjoining window.

A sixth .25 auto. caliber fired cartridge case was found in the master bedroom.

Autopsies of the victims' bodies disclosed the following:

The father had been shot at least twice, with a .25 auto. caliber bullet removed from his head and a .22 caliber bullet from his chest cavity.

The mother had been shot once in the head and a .25 auto. caliber bullet was removed.

The oldest son had been shot twice in the head and two .25 auto. caliber bullets were recovered.

The 16 year old boy had been shot three times, with two .25 auto caliber bullets removed from his head and a .22 caliber bullet from the chest cavity.

The younger son had apparently been shot once but no bullet remained in this body. The daughter had been shot once and a .25 auto. caliber bullet was found in her clothing. In addition, she had been struck a blow in the head with a blunt instrument and the hammer found lying on the couch was believed to be the weapon involved. The hammer fit the damage to the skull and also displayed some apparent blood staining. Any evidence items, clothing and personal effects, were transported to the crime laboratory. A section of the flooring with bloody shoeprints was removed and delivered to the laboratory.

Crime scene analysts also visited the victims' home and obtained items for comparison, such as known writing and printing standards, footwear, and four boxes of .22 caliber fired cartridge cases.

It might be remembered that the crime scene investigators had been assured by the Sheriff's Office that the scene had been properly protected and nothing disturbed prior to their arrival. Imagine their chagrin when the local newspaper carried a front page story featuring a photograph of the Under-Sheriff standing in front of the lodge, holding the hammer in a handkerchief, ala Dick Tracy; obviously a news photo taken before the crime scene team arrived!

II

Background of the Family

Who would want to kill this entire family? The conditions did not indicate a robbery by a passing stranger/intruder, etc. What kind of family was this and did they have any known enemies that might want them dead?

As the investigation progressed, all sources indicated this was a typical upper-middle class family with a lovely and respected mother and four beautiful children. The only possible question mark developed was that of the father.

On the surface, Richard Gooden was a respected businessman and a loyal and responsible father. However, investigation revealed possible inconsistencies in this picture. The first question arose from examination of a religious medal and chain found around his neck at autopsy. He was reportedly a devout Protestant, but the large medallion was that of St. Christopher. Stranger than that, was an inscription on the medal that said "To Richard, my chosen son & heir. Roebert". To this day, no one professes to know who the signatory "Roebert" might be.

The next item to grab the investigators' attention, was the presence of an onion skin copy of a formal typed letter found tucked in a hidden pocket of Richard Gooden's billfold. This letter in question referred to the management of a "world wide organization" by the "Superior Table" and described the organization's goal of "complete peace and unity among all countries of the Earth." The letter indicated the mysterious Mr. Roebert was the director of this group. Further, the letter displayed a secretarial notation at the bottom of the document's dissemination in the typical business manner –

"c.c.   Mr. George
          Mr. Joseph
          Mr. Richard
          Mr. Frank
          Mr. Thomas"

A red check mark was noted alongside the name "Mr. Richard," indicating this was the copy intended for that person. Obviously, Mr. Richard was Richard Gooden, the murder victim. Glancing at the names listed, it is apparent that they are first names, not surnames.

A number of sources confirmed that Richard Gooden had mentioned a Mr. Roberts on several occasions and it was believed that he may be speaking of this same person. Also, Mr. Gooden had informed several individuals that Mr. Roberts was going to pick the family up, for their trip, at the local airport and fly them to their destination in his Lear jet. It was well known that Richard Gooden was a pilot and owned a small single engine Cessna aircraft. Therefore, it was easy to believe that he had a pilot friend, such as Mr. Roberts. In that connection, detectives tracked down every registered Lear jet in the USA and never found any Mr. Roberts, or anyone else possibly connected with the victim!

The name of Mr. Roberts appeared again, according to sources, as one of the partners in a multi-million dollar scheme generated by Richard Gooden. Elaborate plans had been formulated by Gooden to purchase a small suburban airport. The victim told certain people that a combine, he headed, was to provide the money needed for the purchase and subsequent development of a helicopter shuttle service, a large fashionable motel, helipad and air ambulance service, etc. Gooden had talked to a local airport owner in this regard. A check of the personal and company finances revealed no record of any assets of the kind needed for this type of venture. At this point, the idea of Mafia money reared it's ugly head. Could this possibly be the missing link…the factor which caused the mysterious deaths of this family? Part of the investigative effort was directed to follow-up this idea and contacts were established through "racket squad" detectives and their informants to ascertain the viability of this theory.

During this same period, a check of business contacts, records and associates indicated the presence of other problems. Shortly before the murders, Gooden contacted associates and requested an audit of certain records and payments. At one point, he directed no checks from the company be authorized and then later rescinded this directive. It was also learned that he contacted his banker, asking whether or not a check for $200,000 had been deposited to his account, only to be advised that none had been. It was becoming apparent to the detectives that there was something wrong with the financial apparatus of the company and that must be somehow linked to the deaths.

Further investigation of Richard Gooden's activities produced even more puzzling information. On one occasion, he had announced he had to go to San Francisco as part of business ventures and would be away for about a week. The detectives were able to track that trip and learned that Gooden had indeed gone to the West Coast but stayed the entire week in a hotel without apparent contact with anyone. On another occasion he stated that he was required to leave on another out-of-state business trip and that he would be gone for several days. The detectives were able to track him on that trip to the nearby airport. However, they learned he had never flown out but rather stayed several days in a nearby motel, again without apparent contact with anyone!

Richard Gooden was a handsome man, in great physical shape. He was very personable and extremely well liked according to friends and associates. He was also believed to be a near genius and painstakingly careful about business, credit, etc. Several persons described him as being very ambitious and eager to expand his financial ability. One associate even mentioned that Gooden admired famous financiers and had, at one time, remarked that he greatly admired Howard Hughes! He was a pilot, with his own personal small aircraft, and a fancier of expensive horses, having mentioned that he intended to obtain and train quarter-horses. This was allegedly one purpose of the intended trip to Tennessee and Kentucky. Detectives learned that Gooden preferred to carry hard cash, rather than checks, and usually had a large sum of money on his person. They also determined that Mrs. Gooden had a couple of very expensive rings, which she usually wore. No significant amount of money or expensive rings were located about the crime scene or at the home of the victims. Could the motive for the murders have been as simple as robbery?

How about the rest of the family? The mother, Sherry Gooden, was described as a lovely person and a devoted mother. She would not have possibly made an enemy of any kind. Family, friends and neighbors alike admired and respected this lady. The four children, from the younger daughter to the eldest son, were all described as outstanding individuals, excellent students and personable and likeable children and young adults. It was felt, by all concerned, they were strictly innocent victims and no motive could be linked to them, even indirectly.

Initially, investigators felt this crime was probably connected to an individual(s) known to the family, rather than an itinerant burglar or robber. It seemed that if there was a direct link to the family, it had to be through the father. By this time, detectives were traveling throughout the State and various parts of the Country, trying to track down the various theories, based on the father's effects, statements and odd travel habits. The idea of possible involvement of a "secret society," Mafia money, large sums of investment funds, the mysterious Mr. Roberts and the Lear jet, etc. had investigators reeling and dashing off in different directions. As time progressed, all these mystifying theories proved to be a dead end.

Some knowledgeable persons conjectured that Richard Gooden may have had a hidden character flaw; that much of this information was disseminated to build himself up in the eyes of others as something that didn't exist, and to a certain degree was a figment of his imagination. One thing became deadly certain; it had not led to a solution of these terrible crimes.

III

The Alibi and the Suspect

Meanwhile, the lead detectives, John Felton and Howard Summers, were back to the routine screening and interviewing of all persons who had any direct contact with the family. Of course, they were hoping someone might have an idea or information that could provide a fruitful lead in the case. On this particular day, they were interviewing several business associates, one of which was Thomas Scroggins, a business partner and family friend. During a break in the interview, Scroggins asked the officers if they had been able to pinpoint the actual time of the murders. He was aware the press reported the murders occurred long before the bodies were discovered.

During the early part of the investigation, officers had one "good break" when they discovered a neighboring family had been alarmed by a series of gunshots on a particular day, nearly a month before the bodies were discovered, and that they had made note of it and could state with certainty the date of the gunshots. Based on the location, time, and description, officers were certain that the neighbors had heard some of the fatal shots.

Det. Summers advised Scroggins that the Investigators had been able to pin down the date and approximate time the murders were committed. Scroggins then asked in a straight forward manner, "What date was it?" At that point, the detectives glanced inquiringly at one another and the senior officer decided to take a gamble. He told Scroggins the date they were certain the crimes were committed. At that instant, Tom Scroggins began a lengthy and detailed account of his travels and whereabouts on the day in question, from leaving his office in the mid-morning until returning home about 11:30 PM. In other words, he attempted to establish an alibi, without the finger of suspicion having been pointed in his direction, and of course, without being asked to by the officers. As Det. Felton told me on a visit to the Crime Laboratory, "Charlie, I could feel the hair rising on the back of my neck. I looked at my fellow officer and could tell from his eyes, he had the same feeling. We may be talking to the killer!"

Scroggins went on to say that he could remember that particular day very well as it was the day of a record rainfall in the city. Driving was difficult, some underpasses were flooded, along with some housing areas. He recalled that Richard Gooden had asked him to attend the "Builder's Show" at the Civic Center and spend some time with one of their best clients who had a display there. He related that he left home, gassed up and went to the office in mid-morning and drove downtown. There he contacted Joe Rathmann, a vice-president of the firm and checked out the display. He had lunch with Joe and visited with him for part of the afternoon, took in some other displays, and left late in the evening, stopping for a bite to eat on his way home.

He stated further that he went out of his way to drive to Richard Gooden's suburban home and stopped to check it out to insure there was no flood damage apparent in the area. He arrived home, according to the story, about 11:30 PM and went directly to bed.

The officers quickly calculated the approximate time required to drive from the city to Gooden's lodge, commit the murders and return. It was clear that the time covered by Scroggin's alibi was more than adequate to accomplish the deed! Despite their innermost feelings and the mental calculations, the detectives did their very best to not alert Scroggins to their suspicions, but of course making a mental note that a check of this alibi was an urgent priority.

In the meantime, they continued the interview of a routine nature concerning his business relationship with Mr. Gooden and his social relationship with the family. At one point, they inquired if he had any access to firearms. His direct answer to this query turned out to be of considerable interest.

It seemed that he had, a couple of years before, procured two .22 long rifle caliber semi-automatic rifles. These weapons were the type that could be easily "broken-down" and the barrel and receiver stowed in a floating plastic case which also served as the shoulder stock for the rifle. The firearms were technically known as the Armalite model AR-7, sometimes referred to as "the Air Force survival weapon." He was asked if he still had them in his possession and he replied that he didn't; one had been given to a friend in Chicago and the other to a relative. He claimed both were out of his possession for a substantial period of time prior to the homicides.

Scroggins further stated that he had purchased two .25 auto. caliber Beretta semi-automatic pistols, along with two boxes of .25 auto. caliber ammunition from a local firm. When asked about the present location of the pistols, he remarked he had given one to his wife and that he had given the other pistol and two boxes of ammunition to Richard Gooden, his boss.

When the detectives asked whether or not they might be able to examine the Beretta pistol of his wife, he assured them they certainly could and it was delivered to the crime laboratory. Officers also visited the Chicago friend and obtained the AR-7 rifle, still in his possession. It was also delivered to the crime laboratory for examination. The relative pointed out as the recipient of the other rifle, denied ever having it. No one could be found that could verify

33

Gooden as possessing the other pistol or the two boxes of .25 auto. caliber ammo.

At this point, the lead detectives took a step backwards and started to take a closer look at their suspect. They wondered, "just who is this Tom Scroggins, and what exactly was his relationship to the victims?"

Until Scroggins came along, Richard Gooden was the founder and sole executive of the small advertising company. Gooden heard of Scroggins background in a related firm, met him, and was duly impressed. He quickly hired him and soon after, according to associates, began to trust him to handle more and more of the business operation. In fact, it had been announced that Gooden was going to cut Scroggins in for 20% of the business. The investigation disclosed that in the few months prior to the murders, Scroggins had, for all practical purposes, ran the business while Gooden was out of the office much of the time on his various trips. It was of some interest to note, during this time interval, Scroggins had given himself a pay raise on the order of 300%!

Checking with the records of sub-contractors and the company books disclosed that Gooden's company had over-billed certain clients for some time. It appeared this practice started shortly after Scroggins came to the Company. Could this be mere coincidence? Further audits showed that although the company had been paid by some of the clients, in a number of cases the sub-contractors had not received any of the funds. This practice had apparently occurred for a few months prior to the killings. For example: during one period, more than $100,000 had been received by the Company, much of this supposedly to go to sub-contractors, none of whom were paid, but now only a few thousand remained in that account!

When any of these discrepancies were brought to Scroggins attention, he denied any knowledge of the transaction and stated Richard Gooden was probably the only one who could explain them. Of course, Gooden couldn't explain anything, having been murdered weeks before.

Scroggins was asked to take a polygraph (lie detector) examination. He agreed and was actually given two or three tests. Although it is believed that these tests were inconclusive, it was rumored that he had shown some deception indicating possible involvement. Of course, the results of such test, good or bad, are not admissible in court.

During the investigative phase of about a year, the suspect cooperated with the investigating officers in a willing manner. He always had ready answers for most questions. However, if the query involved the homicides directly, Scroggins always professed ignorance and claimed innocence. Although he admitted obtaining some of the unaccounted for funds of the company, he denied he had committed any crimes.

Finally, the detectives unearthed information indicating Richard Gooden had instituted an unannounced audit of certain financial records shortly before the murders. He had left Scroggins with signed blank checks, apparently to care for company business, pay employee salaries, etc. while Gooden and his family were on vacation. But, as a result of this secret audit, he instructed the bank to stop payment on company checks for a time.

It is believed that Gooden had confronted Scroggins by phone on the morning of the murders. Phone records show that Scroggins and Gooden talked four times before 9:45 AM on that fateful day. At that time, the secretary confirmed that Mr. Gooden had told her to call the bank and stop payment on all checks. When Scroggins was asked what he had discussed with Gooden that morning, he advised it was small talk, how's the weather, how's the fishing, how's the family, etc. Scroggins left the office shortly thereafter and never returned that day.

Now the detectives turned to the impromptu alibi. The only telling part, of course, involved the hours spent with the sales executive at the Builder's Show.

They made an appointment and drove out-of-state to a meeting with Joe Rathmann. They told him of the purpose of their visit and immediately asked him if he could recall that day. He asked what day of the week that had been. They advised the date fell on a Friday. He replied almost instantly, "Why, of course I remember that day vividly, that was the day of the record rainfall." At that second, they could hardly hide their frustration as it seemed he was about to validate the suspect's alibi. However, he continued to state, "that was one of the worst storms in my memory and it really loused up our day at the show. In fact, there were hardly any visitors because of the weather and since it was the last day for our display, I told our workers we were wasting our time. So, we broke down the exhibit and were on our way home by mid afternoon".

The excited officers then asked if he could remember Tom Scroggins visit, and he said, "certainly we had a long chat and visited several other displays. We went out to lunch together. But, wait a minute, that couldn't have been Friday, it had to be Thursday, the day before." They inquired how he could be sure, and he stated "I distinctly remember our going to lunch together. It was a beautiful, sunny day and we walked a couple of blocks to a favorite delicatessen. Furthermore, we were breaking down our display when he says he was here checking it out on Friday. It couldn't have been on Friday, that was the day of the horrible storm!"

On the return trip, the detectives carefully reviewed what they knew so far. Destroying the alibi should go a long way in a homicide trial and this unaccounted for time was precisely the time required for Scroggins to be the killer. It looked like things were falling into place. Apparently the suspect had been embezzling funds for some time and Gooden had discovered this fact, confronted the suspect with this information and probably threatened him with exposure to the authorities. Scroggins, they believed, obtained his missing firearms, drove to the lodge, argued with Gooden, probably in an attempt to dissuade him from contacting the police. The officers believed that Scroggins, having failed in this attempt, killed the victim, and the witnesses, the remainder of the family, and then drove back to the city.

The officers knew it would be extremely difficult to place the suspect at the crime scene as the conditions there made this seem unlikely. In addition, the neighbors could not help place him at the scene. No "match" for the bloody footwear impressions had been located. If they were Scroggin's, he had obviously gotten rid of them. The firearms evidence may be helpful, but the suspect attempted to explain that away also.

It was at this point in the investigation, that Felton and Summers took the case file to the Prosecutor of the County for his review. After some study, the Prosecutor advised there was insufficient evidence to charge Scroggins with the murders. The primary shortcoming in the case was that there was no direct evidence to place the suspect at the crime scene. After days and months of investigation, with officers traveling so many miles, chasing so many leads, this was a bitter pill to swallow. But, they vowed to keep chipping away to uncover additional evidence.

Finally, a break came their way when a young neighbor of Scroggins returned from military duty and was made aware of the investigation. He contacted officers and advised he had some information of possible value. He was somewhat of a firearms "junkie" and recalled Scroggins had demonstrated a .22 long rifle caliber, an AR-7, prior to the murders and some time after Scroggins claimed to have disposed of it. Further, he was aware of the fact that Scroggins and other family members used this same rifle to target shoot or "plink" on a makeshift range on family property in another part of the State.

IV

The Forensic Connection

<u>Firearms Identification (Forensic Ballistics)</u>

Immediately upon return from the crime scene, the firearms evidence was turned over to the crime laboratory. As in any unsolved homicide case involving firearms, a priority analysis in this "no gun" case dictated immediate examination. Typically, in a "no gun" case, the items are examined to determine the caliber of firearm involved, the type and manufacturer of ammunition used, and the "class characteristics" of the firearm as displayed on the fired bullets and cartridge cases. Such characteristics on fired bullets include the caliber, the number of lands and grooves (the concentric grooves spiraling through the barrel bore that impart the rotary motion around the bullet's long axis), and the direction of the rifling; i.e., right or left hand. In addition, many manufacturers of firearms utilize lands and grooves with widths different than most others.

Fired cartridge cases also display certain class characteristics of the firearm used. These traits include the type of firing pin, finish markings on the supporting breech of the firearm, the shape, type and location of extractor, ejector mechanisms, etc.

The measurement and comparison of these class markings with known standards from firearms tested in various crime laboratories may provide information on the type and possible manufacturer of the firearm used. If possible, early on in "no gun" homicides, crime laboratory analysts attempt to provide such information to criminal investigators to hopefully lead them to the firearm(s) used in a crime. (See figures 10-12)

In this case, the class characteristics of the .22 long rifle caliber components were not of great assistance in that they were relatively common in nature and included a large group of possible firearms. Although, it was noted in the early examinations, the AR-7 semi-automatic rifle was one of the possibilities.

The class characteristics of the .25 auto. caliber pistol was a more promising story. The markings on the bullets and cartridge cases, taken together, indicated the probable use of a late model .25 auto. caliber Beretta semi-automatic pistol.

Another item of potential assistance was the type of .25 auto. caliber ammunition used. The fired cartridge cases of this caliber displayed no "head stamp" markings of the type routinely seen on American ammunition, and the Berdan primer seen in these cartridge cases also was indicative of foreign manufacture. No specimen of this type had been encountered by the local crime laboratory. The laboratory of the Federal Bureau of Investigation rendered an assist by identifying the ammunition as a recent import to the United States from Finland.

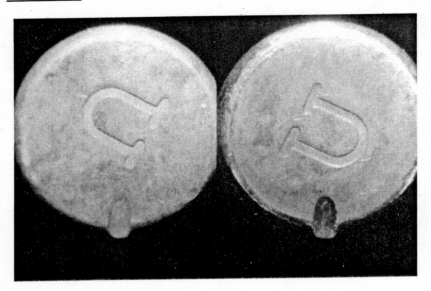

*Fig. 10 – .22 LR caliber cartridge case comparison: evidence left side, test from Chicago AR-7 rifle on right side.

*Fig. 11 – .25 auto. cartridge cases: evidence from scene left side, known Beretta pistol test right side

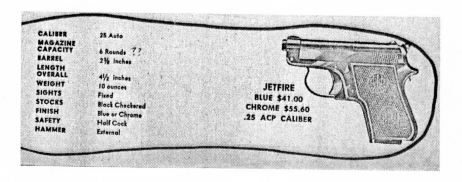

CALIBER	25 Auto
MAGAZINE CAPACITY	6 Rounds 77
BARREL	2⅜ inches
LENGTH OVERALL	4½ inches
WEIGHT	10 ounces
SIGHTS	Fixed
STOCKS	Black Checkered
FINISH	Blue or Chrome
SAFETY	Half Cock
HAMMER	External

JETFIRE
BLUE $41.00
CHROME $55.60
.25 ACP CALIBER

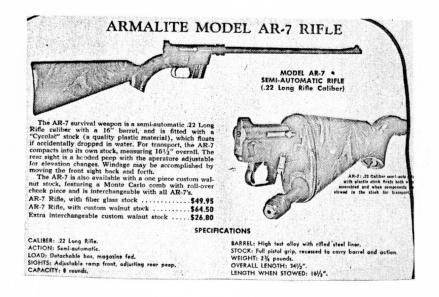

ARMALITE MODEL AR-7 RIFLE

MODEL AR-7
SEMI-AUTOMATIC RIFLE
(.22 Long Rifle Caliber)

The AR-7 survival weapon is a semi-automatic .22 Long Rifle caliber with a 16" barrel, and is fitted with a "Cycolat" stock (a quality plastic material), which floats if accidentally dropped in water. For transport, the AR-7 compacts into its own stock, measuring 16½" overall. The rear sight is a hooded peep with the aperature adjustable for elevation changes. Windage may be accomplished by moving the front sight back and forth.

The AR-7 is also available with a one piece custom walnut stock, featuring a Monte Carlo comb with roll-over cheek piece and is interchangeable with all AR-7's.

AR-7 Rifle, with fiber glass stock $49.95
AR-7 Rifle, with custom walnut stock $64.50
Extra interchangeable custom walnut stock $26.80

AR-7: .22 Caliber semi-auto... with plastic stock floats both... assembled and when components stowed in the stock for transport.

SPECIFICATIONS

CALIBER: .22 Long Rifle.
ACTION: Semi-automatic.
LOAD: Detachable box, magazine fed.
SIGHTS: Adjustable ramp front, adjusting rear peep.
CAPACITY: 8 rounds.

BARREL: High test alloy with rifled steel liner.
STOCK: Full pistol grip, recessed to carry barrel and action.
WEIGHT: 2¾ pounds.
OVERALL LENGTH: 34½".
LENGTH WHEN STOWED: 16½".

*Fig. 12 – Commercial Ads for Firearms Used

41

Within a short period of time, findings of the crime lab and the detectives started to come together in many respects. Analysts were energized by the information regarding the firearms and ammo that had been known to be in the possession of Scroggins.

One interesting development concerned the .22 caliber AR-7 rifles. Analysts had been frustrated in the original search for weapons comparable to the class characteristics of the .22 caliber components. Test standards in laboratory files from an AR-7 rifle displayed a different shape firing pin impression than the evidence fired cartridge cases from the crime scene. However, when detectives brought in the AR-7 from Chicago, it displayed class traits similar in all respects to the evidence items. A check with the manufacturer revealed that the firing pin had been changed for a series of later models. This information indicated the missing AR-7 rifle should have the "right" type of firing pin in like manner. A careful comparison of tests, from the Chicago rifle, was made with the .22 caliber evidence. These comparisons were conducted by examiners using the comparison microscope, an instrument composed of two low powered microscopes linked together with the optical bridge which allows the analyst to see portions of both evidence and test specimens at one time in the same magnified field of vision, separated by a fine "hair line" divider. In this manner, the individual markings imparted to the evidence by forceful contact with imperfections in the bore of the firearm and chamber and breech area of the receiver portion of the rifle, are compared one to the other for similarities or dissimilarities in such markings.

When the individual characteristics are in sufficient agreement the analyst can conclude the bullets and/or cartridge cases were discharged (fired) in the same firearm. In this instance, such markings indicated the Chicago rifle was similar in class but dissimilar individually. In other words, the Chicago rifle was possibly the right-model firearm, but not the actual one used in the crimes.

The .25 auto. caliber Beretta pistol obtained from the suspect's wife was tested in the same fashion. It was found to be in exact agreement as to class traits but dissimilar as to individual characteristics with the .25 auto. caliber bullets and cartridge cases. In other words, this was probably the right kind of pistol, but not the actual one used in the homicides.

The information about the Finnish imported .25 auto. caliber cartridges was of vital importance. Officers were able to determine that the suspect purchased two matching pistols and two boxes of the imported ammo. from a large State firearms distributing house. It was also learned that the two boxes of import ammo. purchased by Scroggins constituted the first ammunition of the kind ever sold in the state at the time of the murders! Although, he claimed to have given the missing pistol and ammunition to the victim, Richard Gooden, no one was ever able to corroborate this "gift".

Now one might consider this probability query? How likely would it be for a murder suspect to possess two matching firearms in two different calibers and types, along with samples of the rare, at this time, ammunition? Further, that one of each firearm duo was inexplicably missing, as was the rare ammo.

Finally, more than a year after the discovery of the bodies, Det. Summers brought to the crime laboratory a large bag, loaded with .22 caliber rim fire brass stained and corroded fired cartridge cases. He explained that a number of investigators, using metal detectors, had searched a makeshift range on Scroggins property for any telltale evidence of the missing AR-7 rifle.

Using the stereoscopic microscope, the cartridge cases were screened for class characteristics, primarily of the firing pin impression. Twenty-one were selected for further examination and carefully cleaned under the stereomicroscope. Of this group, one was eliminated from consideration, fifteen were found to be similar to the evidence fired cartridge cases from the crime scene, but were too stained and corroded to be further identified. Five of the fired cartridge cases from the Scroggins property were identified as having been fired in the same firearm as those from the crime scene. In other words, there were sufficient individual characteristics remaining to allow for this conclusion on the part of the analyst. In addition to notes on the examination, photomicrographs (photos taken through the microscope) were taken of certain markings, some of the major individual markings used in the comparison. These photographs, taken through the comparison microscope optics, show markings side-by-side, separated by a fine line, of the kind considered by the examiner in his examination. In this case, due to their importance, an enlarged display of the firearms evidence and certain markings was prepared for use by the Prosecutor and possible use in court should there be a trial. (see Figs. 13-14)

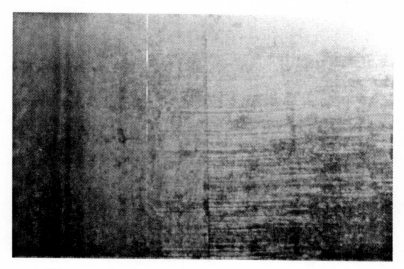

*Fig. 13 – Chamber markings on sides of .22 cartridge cases; evidence left, known from suspect's range on right side.

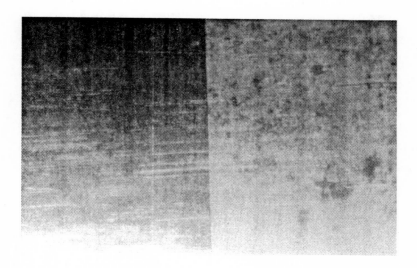

*Fig. 14 – Additional chamber markings as above.

As those familiar with firearms know, when the firing pin strikes the rim of a rim fire cartridge, such as the .22 long rifle caliber, it partially crushes the rim causing discharge, and in so doing it often leaves fine impressed and sometimes striated markings in the crushed area. Such a blow by the firing pin also often produces fine impressed markings on the underside of the rim. In many cases, these markings may assist in the positive identification of the firearm involved. When discharge of the cartridge occurs, the gases inside the cartridge expand causing increased pressures in all directions. These forward pressures drive the bullet down the barrel of the firearm. They also push the cartridge case rearward and may cause finish markings from the firearm breech to be imprinted on the head of the case. As these pressures are exerted sideways, they expand the cartridge case creating a snug fit against the chamber walls. As the case is forcibly extracted/withdrawn from the chamber, imperfections in the chamber wall often cause lengthy striated markings (fine valleys and ridges of microscopic nature) on the sides of the case. These markings may be sufficiently individual in nature to allow for identification of the weapon used. And, as the extraction and ejection operation ensues, those parts of the firearm may cause comparable markings to be imparted to the head and rim of the cartridge case. In this case, the primary markings used for comparison were found in the firing pin impression and the chamber markings on the case sides.

Needless to say, the lead investigators Dets. Felton and Summers, were overjoyed at the results and felt this was the "coup de grace" they needed to get this one to trial. They picked up a copy of the report and photocopies to show the Prosecutor.

The Casebook and the Prosecutor

The lead detectives, Felton and Summers, assembled a 700 page Casebook listing all the known facts, witnesses, statements, and evidence for the authorities. The book included the following:

(1) Original reports of the crime discovery.

(2) The crime scene search, physical evidence, photos, etc.

(3) The autopsy reports and evidence recovered therein.

(4) Background aspects of the investigation.

(5) The phony alibi of the suspect.

(6) Incriminating statements of the suspect.

(7) Phone call records.

(8) Evidence of fraud and theft by the suspect.

(9) Results of polygraph tests.

(10) Results of the Firearms Identification (Forensic Ballistics) comparisons.

The officers turned the Casebook over to the Prosecuting Attorney and reviewed the salient facts with him, requesting a warrant for

Thomas Scroggins on a charge of "Murder in the 1ˢᵗ Degree." The Prosecutor advised he would take the matter under advisement and get back to them shortly.

After a delay of some duration, the Prosecutor advised the detectives that he did not feel he could charge Scroggins at this time. He stated further that his decision was based on the fact that they could not place him personally at the crime scene; there were no fingerprints, etc. He promised that in the event further evidence was discovered he would review the facts again.

The officers were shocked and confused. They felt they had a convincing case; motive, opportunity, time line, a false alibi, possession of one of the murder weapons, etc. They were certain that if they could get it to a jury, a conviction would result. Furthermore, it was extremely difficult to understand the reluctance of the Prosecutor to charge Scroggins.

Nevertheless, the officers were stalemated at this point, after some 15 months of investigation. As one detective put it later, "the main thing I got out of this case was an ulcer."

However, there is often "more than one way to skin a cat." In the State, there had been several cases where, for some reason, a Prosecuting Attorney had declined to try a case and the State's Attorney General had appointed a special prosecutor to try the case. The officers were well acquainted with a prosecuting attorney from a populous county downstate who had a reputation as arguably the best in the state. They contacted him and asked him to review, he told them "if I can't get a conviction in this case, I will give up the practice." Further, he remarked he would take vacation time and do it on his own time with the permission of his boss., the Chief Prosecutor. Permission was quickly granted and a formal request was directed to the Attorney General. After a short review, the Attorney General, without comment, rejected the request. They had thought this was a formality and that this time there would be justice in this case. They were wrong again. They were back to square one.

This case was complicated by the fact that the County Sheriff and Prosecutor had apparently taken the position that this crime was too complicated for only one person to be involved. Missing cash and rings from the effects of the victims still spelled "Robbery" to them. Some officers felt a local caretaker, who assisted in discovery of the bodies, may have been responsible. He had a reputation for being temperamental and a little weird. The attitude of the Sheriff's Dept. might be summed up by the statement of one of their detectives, some years later, who said "We can't take all the evidence that's available and say Scroggins did it and forget about the whole thing. I don't think it was ever that clearly established."

To quote the vernacular, "the perp walked." Although, it's deplorable when it rears it's ugly head, it also appears that there may have been some jurisdictional friction between the Sheriff's Department and the State Police. As an example of this possibility, years after the case was officially stalled, a special anniversary account appeared in a large city paper. The case was described as an "open" murder investigation and the Sheriff of the County was quoted as saying "the .22 caliber casings found at Scroggins firing range matched casings found at the murder scene, but individual markings differed!" The fact is that this same Sheriff received the original report from the Crime Laboratory, which stated in part "...at least five of the above listed shells (cartridge cases from the Scroggins range) were fired in the same weapon as the four .22 caliber shells from the crime scene," (emphasis added). This indicated the missing AR-7 rifle of Scroggins was one of the murder weapons. It can only be hoped the Sheriff was misquoted by the press.

Efforts to produce additional evidence and/or other suspects continued for several years. During this period, the State Police Detective Division was headed by one of several Chief of Detectives who were only satisfied with homicide cases that were brought to a successful conclusion and detectives who were considered tough and efficient. It was reported that on more than one occasion, detectives left on assignments directly from the Chief with the instructions "Don't come back to Headquarters until you are successful." It is rumored that there are a couple of detectives still missing!

However, for some time, it would appear to an outsider that Scroggins had little awareness that he had been under suspicion and accusations. At least outwardly, it didn't seem to bother him too much.

The Decision and Its Aftermath

As the refusal of the Prosecuting Attorney and Attorney General to charge their suspect sank in, it became apparent to the investigators that unless something dramatic turned up, the investigation was up against the wall. The state of the case was summed up in an editorial special feature that appeared nearly 2 ½ years after the murder in the State's largest newspaper with a bold type headline "The Unsolved Gooden Case." The article was subtitled "A New Startling Report on the Bizarre Events and Strange Dealings that Foreshadowed Murder." As in a number of articles that had been printed over time, Scroggins was cited as the main suspect, but the end conclusion was that the evidence was insufficient to warrant arrest.

In the meantime, the publicity and references, at least outwardly, didn't appear to affect Thomas Scroggins that much. During the immediate aftermath, of the discovery of the gruesome murders, Scroggins had effectively taken control of the company business. It might be of interest to note that approximately eight months prior to the deaths, the business had been evaluated at a worth of about $600,000! After the deaths, during the selling of the estate, this same business was sold by a bank receivership for $3,500.00! It should not be surprising to learn that the purchaser was Tom Scroggins. It was also of interest to learn that for a time, during the period immediately after the murders, Scroggins had been able to obtain a lucrative advertising contract from the same large firearms distributor that had sold him the matching Beretta pistols and Finnish ammunition! Sometime later this firm cancelled the contract, informing interested parties that the business had overcharged them and had failed to pay the sub-contractors! It seemed that investigators had heard this complaint before. Could it be that Scroggins was a master manipulator or con artist? He, of course, denied any wrong doing or breaking the law.

For nearly five years after the family murders, Scroggins apparently tended to business and shrugged off various queries about the deaths and any involvement he may have had. Over this time he was interviewed by a number of police investigators and many press and news reporters. He readily admitted that he was a prime suspect in the "unsolved" murders, but steadfastly denied any connection with the deaths, any knowledge of the "secret society," any knowledge of the mysterious Mr. Roberts, and any knowledge concerning the illicit business practices or the large amount of missing funds.

The case is technically listed as an "Open Murder." The lead detectives, at least, consider it "solved" although not complete.

THE EPILOGUE

Approximately five years after the murders, Thomas Scroggins used the remaining Beretta pistol to commit suicide. He left a neatly printed note, which has been widely quoted in the press, and which stated in effect that he was a liar, cheat, and a phony, but not a killer. What was not reported was that the note also displayed, apparently as an afterthought, in a contrasting and almost illegible scrawl, the words "Dear God Forgive Me."

THE EX-COP KILLER

I

The Victim and the Ballistics Evidence

It was a rainy night and rather cool for central Florida. Deputy Al Richter was returning to his office, having completed his tour of duty. On the outskirts of town, at the location of the building supply parking lot, he noticed a late model car parked in the empty lot at an unusual angle and with the driver's window apparently rolled down. He pulled into the lot and stopped behind the car to check it out. As he approached the driver's side, he played his light into the car and was surprised to see a man slumped over the wheel. The officer could see a trail of dried blood coursing down the man's face and chin. It appeared to come from a darkened hole in his left cheek. The man had apparently been shot and was dead. There was no firearm to be seen and it looked like the deputy may have a murder on his hands.

A call was placed to the Sheriff's Office requesting assistance from detectives, crime scene investigators and the Medical Examiner's Office. A search of the car revealed no evidence of a struggle and the Deputy Medical Examiner found the victim's billfold in his trousers pocket with normal identification and containing $86.in bills. Apparently, no robbery was indicated.

A search of the area around the car revealed only one item of interest, a .45 Auto. caliber fired cartridge case. Measurements and photographs were taken and the casing was carefully lifted and placed in a small plastic evidence bag. The bag was sealed and marked for identification by the crime scene investigator. It would be transferred to the State Crime Laboratory at the earliest time for possible fingerprints and firearms identification.

The body of the victim, Dave Townsend, a local insurance adjuster, was removed by medical examiner staff and transported to the County Morgue. The hands had been covered with plastic bags to insure no potential trace evidence would be lost and the entire body was encased in a plastic zippered bag.

The following morning, Dr. James Hendrix, the County Medical Examiner, performed an autopsy on Mr. Townsend. The only trauma to the body was that of the gunshot wound. The victim, in his 30's, had been in good health and there was no question but that the sole cause of his death was one gunshot that traveled from below his left eye, upwards and backwards, behind the eye orbit, into the cranial cavity and portions of his brain. The bullet was in fragments and pieces, and was different than any the medical examiner had previously encountered. The particles consisted of fragments of copper bullet jacket and numerous fine lead shot. The doctor, a forensic pathologist, was familiar with firearms and ammunition and he thought he knew what he had found. A cartridge had been developed and produced in several handgun calibers, commercially known as "the Glaser Safety Slug." This projectile utilized a jacketed bullet with fine shot in place of the standard lead core. It was claimed that it had been developed for police use so that if it were fired at a criminal and missed, striking and deflecting from a metal post, sidewalk, etc, it would break up rather than ricochet and thereby not constitute a threat to an innocent bystander. It was also claimed that the "Safety Slug" was a very lethal projectile as it would not over-penetrate the body, but would break-up and spread thereby using it's energy within vital areas of the body of a victim. This particular cartridge, at this point in time, was most often seen in police circles. The medical examiner, after explaining this theory to the investigators, placed the fragments in a sealed and marked vial for transfer to the crime lab. The officers were told to get confirmation of the bullet type from the "ballistics section."

The very next day, a member of the Sheriff's Evidence Section delivered the fired cartridge case from the scene and the fragments of the bullet from the victim to the Firearms Section of the Regional State Crime Laboratory.

$$\boxed{\text{II}}$$

The Firearms & Toolmark Identification Section

Crime Laboratories are typically composed of Units where specially trained analysts practice in one or more of the disciplines of Forensic Science. This practice is often referred to as "Criminalistics" or the application of the instruments and methods of physical science to the solution of crime. One such Unit would be the Firearms and Toolmark Identification Unit. In this part of the Crime Laboratory, analysts are concerned with the examination and comparative analysis of firearms and ammunition components and other tools and the markings they produce.

Although, it is generally considered a misnomer, in many regions of the world this type of analysis had long been called "forensic ballistics." It sounds more glamorous than "Firearms Identification", the preferred term. Actually, ballistics is defined as the study of the motion of a projectile and which includes all the actions and reactions that occur with a firearm from the moment the firing pin or striker is released, through the discharge of the cartridge, the travel of the projectile through the barrel, it's flight path or trajectory, and impact on the target.

These various reactions and measurements are usually described as "interior, exterior, and terminal ballistics."

In this country, during the 1920s, a group of individual scientists and ordnance experts were responsible for the origins of modern firearms and ammunition comparisons, especially using the "comparison microscope." This group, headed by Col. Calvin Goddard, a medical doctor, surgeon, and ordnance officer, adopted the term "forensic ballistics" to describe their function and it is still thought of as an adjunct to the original term "ballistics," even today.

In a case such as this one, very early in the investigation, officers will deliver the firearms evidence to the proper unit of the crime lab. Here analysts will compare the bullet(s) and cartridge case(s) with known standards and data from their files and recorded data furnished by the Federal Bureau of Investigation in order to determine the possible type and manufacturer of the ammunition, and possible type and maker of the firearm used. This was done with the bullet fragments from the victim and the cartridge case found alongside the car.

Based on these comparisons, the detectives were advised the ammunition was .45 Auto. caliber and involved the "Glaser Safety Slug" bullet as predicted by the medical examiner. In addition, the "class characteristics" of the firearm imparted to the bullet jacket; that is, the number of lands and grooves, the concentric remnants of the original barrel bore and associated recessed areas, cut, etched, or impressed grooves, spiraling through the barrel, the comparative widths of these lands and groves, and the direction of their inclination or twist, were determined. The evidence cartridge case also exhibited gross and microscopic markings caused by the firing pin, the extractor, the ejector, breech area and other parts of the pistol action. The location and type of these traits are helpful in determining the kind of firearm used. In some cases, these "family traits" can actually pinpoint the type and make of firearm. In the majority of cases, they will provide a short list of possible firearms for the investigators to concentrate their search for possible weapons.

In this case, the detectives were advised the firearm was probably a Colt semi-automatic pistol, of the type used by our military for many years, or a copy of this pattern made by one of several other manufacturers. It was also pointed out that the Glaser Safety Slug was an uncommon type of ammunition, used mostly by police officers.

III

The Suspect and the "Ballistics" Evidence

At first, the officers were stymied in their search for a suspect. The victim had a decent reputation and would not have enemies that wanted him dead. Further, there was no indication of armed robbery or car-jacking. But then they learned that Dave Townsend had fallen in love with an attractive local woman and they were seen together on a number of occasions. The detectives were well aware that high on the list of homicide motives were love triangles and/or unrequited love. They sought out the girlfriend and interviewed her at length.

She told them that she had been dating Dave Townsend and that it had developed into a serious relationship. Of even greater interest was information that she had broken up with a long time boyfriend not long ago. She further advised detectives that her former boyfriend, Steve Shindler, was extremely jealous and was visibly upset over her new lover. She understood that Steve and Dave had a bitter argument about the relationship.

The officers were well acquainted with Steve Shindler. He had served on two different police agencies as a patrol and undercover officer and currently was employed as an instructor for the Regional Police Training Academy!

Although police officers hate to think of another cop as a suspect in a serious crime, they know their ranks are not immune and don't let their personal feelings interfere with the investigation. So, doubting that the lead of Shindler would take them anywhere, they pursued this trail, just in case.

The initial interview with Shindler was unproductive. He had an alibi for his time during the commission of the murder, although the alibi was one of those hard to prove or disprove. The detectives asked him whether or not he owned a .45 Auto. caliber pistol. He produced a "Permit to Carry" from his billfold and a Star .45 Auto. caliber pistol from under his car seat.

The Spanish made Star pistol had a barrel rifled with six lands and grooves, right-hand twist. The officers were aware that the evidence bullet jacket fragments displayed rifling engraving of six lands and grooves with a left-hand twist, consistent with the Colt pattern pistol (see Fig. 15). But to be safe, they asked if they could take the pistol for testing and Shindler readily agreed. Coincidentally, a department officer had advised investigators that he had worked with Steve Shindler some years before and recalled Steve carried a Colt .45 at that time. So, the detectives asked Shindler if he owned a Colt pistol and he replied that he sold it to a young officer from another agency about 9 years ago. After this much time, he couldn't recall the name of the officer or which agency he had worked for.

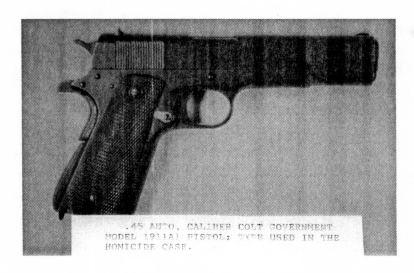

*Fig. 15 - .45 Auto. caliber Colt pistol

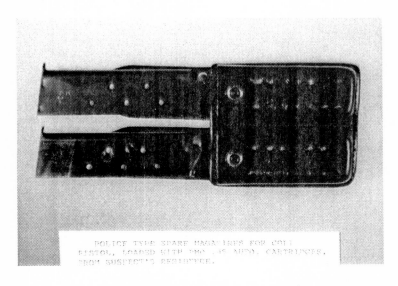

*Fig. 16 – Spare magazines from suspect's home

Now the lukewarm lead had turned red hot. Officers sought and obtained a search warrant for Shindler's double-wide mobile home. The search turned up some firearms material, but no Colt pistol. However, the searchers seized a box of .45 Auto. caliber fired cartridge cases. As many shooters and police officers do, Shindler "saved brass" for re-loading purposes. They also confiscated two magazines (clips) fully loaded with live .45 Auto. caliber cartridges, and their black leather holsters. The officers noted that these magazines appeared similar to standard Colt issue and they inquired about this fact. Shindler replied that he had forgotten to give these to the young officer he had sold the pistol to and that he had them lying on a shelf for about 9 years. The following day these items were delivered to the Crime Lab. for any possible comparisons that could be made with the crime scene evidence (see Fig. 16).

The Forensic Connection

Recently, there has been a vastly increased interest in forensic science. The word "forensic" is derived from the Latin word "forum," loosely translated as a legal debate or argument. "Forensic Science" has been defined simply as "Science in the Courtroom."

In this case, the physical evidence was entirely related to the discipline of Firearms Identification. First, the box of fired cartridge cases or "saved brass" was compared to the .45 Auto. caliber fired case found next to the victim's car. The fired cases from Shindler's mobile home, were determined, to have been fired in the same pistol as the crime scene cartridge case. A number of class and individual characteristic markings were found to be in agreement. The most dramatic markings were located on the head of the cartridge cases (lay persons often refer to this area as the base). When a pistol is fired, the chamber pressures that drive the bullet from the barrel and on to it's target also rams the head of the case against the supporting breech of the pistol. Gross and fine tool markings and imperfections in the breech area are often impressed into the softer metal of the cartridge case head. These markings are typically referred to as "breech face markings." They often are sufficiently unique to allow for positive identification of the individual firearm. This was the case with these comparisons (see Figs. 17-18).

*Fig. 17 – Box of fired cartridge cases from suspect

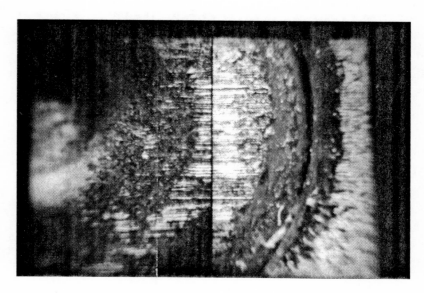

*Fig. 18 – Breechface markings comparison; crime scene case
left; cartridge case from suspect's box on right.

It was also observed that all of the live ammunition in the confiscated magazines were headstamped with the PMC logo. This mark was the registered trademark of Pan Metal Corp., a South Korean firm. When such cartridges are formed, most manufacturers headstamp their cases with a caliber designator and some form of company logo or numerical indicator. This process usually leaves distinctive impressed toolmarks from the die used to form the headstamp. Although thousands of cases may be stamped with the same die, it usually occurs within a brief time frame. This information can be very helpful in tracing certain ammunition. Side-by-side microscopic comparisons also revealed that many of the fired cases from the "saved brass" stash also were of PMC manufacture and displayed toolmarks indicative of manufacture on the same die (see Fig. 19).

The clincher for the laboratory analyst came when he contacted a technical representative from PMC. After being advised of the investigation of the ammunition connection, the company representative asked, "How long ago did this Shindler fellow say he got rid of the Colt pistol?" When told that the suspect claimed it was about 9 years ago, the representative remarked "That's very interesting, especially since we have manufactured and exported that cartridge into the United States for less than 5 years!"

*Fig. 19 – Headstamp defects; cartridge case from suspect's box left side; cartridge from spare magazine right side.

Sequel to the Case

Before Steve Schindler could be tried and convicted, he disappeared. For two years, investigators searched diligently for the ex-cop. Over time, they received cooperation from the former girlfriend. She informed them that she had been receiving regular long distance phone calls from Shindler, apparently from out-of-state. The officers received permission from her and the court to "eavesdrop" and record phone calls. Careful scrutiny of the calls revealed indications of the type of work Shindler was engaged in performing. From certain comments and background noise, they developed several out-of-state locations as possibilities. Officers from several jurisdictions assisted them in their search. On one busy work day, Shindler was spotted walking to his car, arrested, and ultimately extradited to Florida to stand trial.

In the interim, he had picked a name from a city newspaper obituary column, sent for and received a new Social Security card, obtained a valid driver's license and obtained employment under the assumed identity. He, it is claimed, was totally surprised and dismayed by his arrest. He is currently serving life in prison.

THE TROOPER AND THE SHOVEL

The B&E (Breaking & Entering) Investigation

Trooper Schmidt was on single man patrol about mid-morning. He was driving painted patrol car unit #235. Harry Schmidt had been a State Police Trooper for about five years. He was known to be a very conscientious officer, mentally keen, and physically fit. He had been happily married for several years. It was a beautiful summer day and traffic on the main highway was comparatively light. Just as Harry was hoping this would not be a boring day on patrol, the radio signaled a call to his patrol unit.

The desk Corporal, back at the Post, advised him that a call had been received concerning an overnight burglary at a small tool and die shop located in his assigned patrol area. He told the Post he was "clear" on the message and headed 235 in the direction of the burglarized business. In a short time, he had made original contact with the plant owner.

The owner advised him of the discovery and provided a list of several missing items. He also pointed out the place of forcible entry and the location of the "cash box" that had been ransacked. The Trooper made notes on this information, took photographs, and dusted several areas for latent fingerprints. He finally asked the owner if he was aware of any possible suspects. To his surprise, the owner advised that several days before the burglary a stranger had walked, unannounced, into the shop, walked around, and appeared to be showing more than a casual interest in the operation. When he was approached, the stranger stated he was merely looking for a job and was hoping he could apply. When told there were no openings, he left without further words. The victim stated further that he felt the man, a white male, thin build, about 40s, seemed to act suspiciously. He copied down the stranger's car license number on a desk scratch pad, but he had inadvertently discarded it. The Trooper asked to see the pad and using side lighting he observed faint indentations in the paper from the prior top pages. He utilized an old investigative trick and lightly brushed carbon pencil shavings over the indented area restoring the registration number!

A quick call to the Post produced information on the car registration showing it was issued to a late model Cadillac sedan and named the owners and their address in a small village in the Post patrol district. Harry thought there was probably nothing of importance to this lead but decided as a matter of routine to check it out. He headed #235 for the village, mentally calculating he had sufficient remaining time on his shift to check out the car and return to the Post.

As Harry entered the village, he turned the patrol car into a service station on Main St. He introduced himself to the attendant and inquired if he knew the Cadillac's registered owners. The attendant surely did, the couple were somewhat elderly and retired, an upright and well-liked couple. The Trooper thought this investigation was going to be another "bum steer," but now that he was here, he may as well contact the folks. Having learned the location of the address, he drove over. He got out of the patrol car and then realized he hadn't checked out of radio service or advised the Post desk officer of his location, as procedures required. Oh well, he thought, this will only take a minute and then I'll be in service and on my way back to the Post.

The Disappearance

What Trooper Schmidt didn't know was that the old folks weren't home. They were on an extended vacation trip to another state. However, the home was occupied by a tall, thin, white man in his 40s; a nephew of the old couple. He had recently appeared on their doorstep after many years of non-contact. They were vaguely aware that he had been in some kind of trouble with the law in another state, where his family had originally lived. They felt sorry for him, let him stay at their home and drive the one car while they were away.

What the old couple didn't know was that the nephew had a long criminal record in a couple of other states, including arrests and convictions for breaking and entering, armed robbery and assault, and attempted murder. They were not aware of the fact that the nephew, Alvin Kennedy, had recently been released on parole despite a recorded warning from the prison psychiatrist that Kennedy was a sociopath and was liable to kill someone!

The Trooper walked onto the front porch and rang the doorbell. The door opened to reveal Alvin Kennedy, standing inside with a 9 mm caliber German Luger pistol pointed at the officer's chest.

Trooper Harry Schmidt never contacted his dispatcher and never returned to his Post.

The last person, other than Alvin Kennedy, to see Trooper Schmidt alive was a young girl from the village who later was interviewed by investigating officers.

She told them she had seen the Trooper driving his painted patrol unit out of the town with Mr. Kennedy sitting in the back seat of the patrol car behind the officer. At that point, car #235 and Trooper Harry Schmidt disappeared.

After some time had elapsed, the Post desk officer tried to contact car #235 by radio, but received no answer to repeated calls. The Corporal knew the officer had followed up on the B&E investigation with a request for registration information on a certain plate number and this info had been dispatched to the patrol unit. He now sent a 2-man patrol unit to the village to see if anyone there had seen the Trooper. They found no one at the address, and the Cadillac missing.

The patrol unit and Trooper Harry Schmidt had effectively disappeared. Thus began one of the biggest manhunts in the history of the State. Search parties of police officers, firemen, Boy Scouts, and other volunteers spread out in an ever widening radius from the village. The search was hampered by the fact that this area of the State, although near population centers, was sparsely inhabited and consisted of numerous large woodlots, a number of large swales and swampy areas, interspersed with old farms, some abandoned. There was a lot of difficult ground to cover and no leads to follow.

Finally, aerial search discovered the patrol car, mired down in an old muddy bean field. Investigators examined #235 and the surrounding area for any physical evidence. Several partial footwear impressions were noted but exhibited insufficient detail for positive identification. Search parties now began a new search pattern with the patrol car at the center of the circle.

During the same time frame, investigators determined that the old couple also owned a small cabin in the northern part of the state. This vacation site was located and the Cadillac was seen parked next to the cabin. Officers crept to the cabin, entered quickly, catching Alvin Kennedy asleep and overcoming him before he could grab the .38 Special caliber revolver lying on the stand next to the bed. The revolver displayed a stamped logo and number indicating it was the issue revolver of Trooper Schmidt.

A search of the Cadillac produced a short-handle shovel from the trunk. A member of the Crime Laboratory search team seized the shovel as evidence, taking care to preserve fresh appearing soil from the shovel blade. Although it may have no bearing on the case, the soil traces presented an ominous suggestion.

III

The Suspect

Alvin Kennedy turned out to be very con-wise and uncooperative. The investigators now feared the worse. The weather was very hot and they felt that even if the Trooper had been kidnapped and possibly handcuffed to a tree or something similar, he couldn't last long without water. Pleading, threats, trickery, all yielded negative results with the suspect, who wouldn't give them the time of day.

Kennedy, as the records disclosed, had spent much of his adult life in prison. He was apparently a sociopath, knew his way around the Criminal Justice System, and was the perfect "jail house lawyer" type. He appeared to relish "winning" the contest between himself and police authority. Another example of the many recidivists from our system of Corrections and Criminal Justice. As veteran officers reviewed his records, they shook their heads in disbelief that a parole board could release this individual based on his record and the warning of the prison psychiatrist. Based on what they knew in this case, he had to be the person responsible for the Trooper's disappearance. Yet, it was difficult to understand why he would abduct a police officer and possibly kill him over a simple felony.

The answer came from an off-shoot of this investigation when detectives discovered there had been a burglary of a small factory in the Northern town near the old couple's cabin. In that burglary, a watchman had been murdered and they could place Alvin Kennedy in the area at the time of the crime. The Method of Operation (Modus Operandi – MO) in that case matched the one Trooper Schmidt had been investigating. They now felt that the suspect must have believed that the Trooper was following the murder connection and panicked.

The State Police officers were at their wits end. Time was running out with the hot dry summer days and the trooper would not live long. Kennedy would not tell them anything. Then Trooper Schmidt's wife came forward and asked the Commissioner if she could be allowed to talk to the suspect. This was an unusual request that they wouldn't normally favor, but feeling they had nothing to lose and there still was a possibility the Trooper's life could be in the balance, the officers agreed.

Imagine their shock and dismay when Kennedy agreed to talk with Mrs. Schmidt and then agreed to lead the officers to her husband.

IV

The Forensic Connection — Toolmarks

Arrangements were quickly made to isolate the area described by the suspect. A square mile surrounding the site was cordoned off and officers stationed to keep out the curious and the media until the Trooper was removed and the scene searched for physical evidence.

The suspect was transported to the area, by detectives, followed by a crime scene crew from the State Police and Dept. of Health Crime Laboratories. During the trip it became clear why searching parties had not found the missing officer. Apparently Kennedy had taken care of the Trooper and then moved the patrol car miles away to avoid detection and discovery of the officer. The search center had not been based solely on discovery of the abandoned patrol car. Near the car was a small clear water creek traversing the property. A member of the searching team had discovered a couple of nickel-plated .38 Special caliber fired cartridge cases lying partly hidden under several inches of water. A rush delivery of these items to the Crime Lab and a comparison with test fired cartridge cases revealed what the officers feared was in fact true. The casings found in the creek bed had been fired in the missing Trooper's revolver!

The new area of interest was a deeply wooded section broken by a few swales, on the back portion of a large farm. The old farmhouse became an Operations Center for the time being. Several key investigators and the Crime Lab search crews were appointed to accompany the suspect. The Operations Center was staffed by a number of officers, including the Commissioner, the Commanding Officer of the Uniform Division, and the Chief of Detectives. They were all determined that the area of the actual crime scene would be preserved for a proper search and not trampled by curious officers or the media.

Kennedy led the search party along an old fence line and down the border of an old orchard into a dense wooded area. On the hike, he claimed he had not wanted to harm the Trooper and had taken a rope with them so that he could tie him to a tree. But, once into this area, he claimed the Trooper bolted and started to run and he had to shoot him. Of course, no rope was ever found, and examination of the Trooper's uniform shirt and entrance wound indicated the shot was fired with the barrel nearly touching the officer! Along a brush line he pointed out what appeared to be a small pile of limbs and old vegetation as the location of the body, which was partly buried and partly covered.

After initial photographs and measurements were taken, the Coroner assisted officers in carefully removing the brush from the body. The partly decomposed body was that of Trooper Harry Schmidt. He was clad only in under shorts and undershirt. There was evidence of an entrance bullet wound in the back of the victim's neck. But, where was the rest of his gear – his uniform, cap, holster, Sam Browne belt, etc? A member of the search team called for assistance andpointed to an area on the edge of a nearby swale where he noticed some of the fine-grain clay soil had recently been disturbed. Careful exploration and excavation of the site revealed most of the Trooper's uniform and equipment buried a short distance underground.

At this site, a couple of clods of dried soil were noted to be relatively intact and displayed a shape indicative of falling off a shovel blade. In addition, one clod in particular displayed numerous striated markings, parallel miniature valleys and ridges or surface contours, apparently caused by imperfections in the tip of the shovel blade. This soil, along with some of the loose deposits adjacent thereto was carefully collected, preserved, and photographed in detail. A couple of pails were brought to the site and filled with moist clay from the burial ground and all was brought back to the Crime Laboratory.

In the Laboratory, samples of soil from the shovel were compared with known samples from the scene and found to be indistinguishable from one another (see Fig. 20). Of course, this type of comparison would not be that definitive. But then, the shovel was used to make tool markings in samples of known soil from the scene. When an instrument such as a shovel is used, imperfections on the cutting edge of the blade tip from the manufacturing processes, and later use and abuse of the tool, create minute parallel surface contours which are unique to that particular shovel and which can be compared to similar tool marks left at the crime scene. In this case, striated markings on the clod of soil from the scene and test markings made with the shovel blade were strikingly similar and there could be no doubt that this shovel had been used to bury the officer's gear. Such evidence is deemed to be more reliable than "eye-witness" testimony and even "statements against the interests of the accused" require corroboration and physical evidence rates high on any such lists (see Fig. 21).

Some officers, however, remained puzzled by one aspect. Trooper Schmidt was known to be quick, strong, athletic and unafraid. They wondered why he hadn't made a break for it or jumped his assailant. It is felt that there is little doubt that Kennedy "conned" the Trooper into believing that he wouldn't be harmed if he went without a struggle. History has demonstrated that his wasn't the first or the last time a competent officer had fallen for this type of "con."

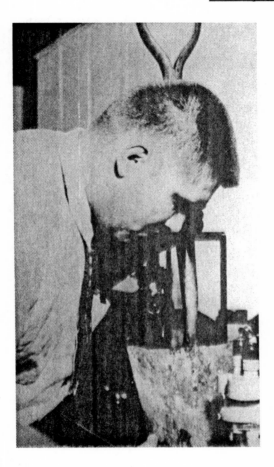

*Fig. 20 – Author with shovel from defendant's car trunk

*Fig. 21 – Toolmarks in soil comparison; underlying enlarged photograph of soil clump from crime scene; overlay photograph of test markings made with the shovel.

Sequel to the Case

As with many injustices of the criminal justice system, this case had it's problems. The defendant waived a jury trial and then pleaded guilty before the judge to a charge of 2nd degree murder. After serving a moderate term in state prison, he was once again paroled!

Later, he broke into a home, tied the victims, and left them briefly as he obtained an axe from a tool crib. It is believed that he was about to chop them up! During his absence, the male victim was able to work free of his bonds, grappled with Kennedy upon his return, wrestled a revolver from the criminal's waistband, and shot and wounded him in the side. Alvin escaped but was soon captured and returned to prison, hopefully this time for good.

THE GRAVE DIGGER

I

The Bird Dog

Bill Fosmore took advantage of this beautiful fall day to train his German Shorthair. It was just before the pheasant season, when State law allows one to run his bird dog without firearms. This dog had a great nose and it was a thrill to see him hold point on a bird. However, she had broken her hold on a pheasant and ranged a short distance away to the edge of the woods, near a footpath into this little used forest area. Here, she circled a spot, appeared agitated, and whined softly. As Bill got to the place, he noticed soil and dried leaves that appeared to be disturbed and in particular several leaves "glued" together by several small brownish-coated splotches. He was a long time dog trainer and hunter and he knew dried blood when he saw it, and he was uncomfortable about his dog's actions. He carefully marked the spot with a broken and pointed bough stuck in the loosened dirt.

Bill left the location, went to his car and drove to the nearest public phone to call the Sheriff's Office. Officers followed him to the scene and removed some of the loosened soil to a depth of about 18 to 24 inches, until they uncovered a hand and wrist. They then ceased the operation and called for help from the state crime laboratory and the coroner's office. The County Coroner advised he would respond personally and deputies waited for him and the laboratory crime scene searchers to arrive.

In this suburban county, the coroner was a forensic pathologist, considered by many police to be one of, if not the very best in this discipline. He was not only good at what he does, but he was extremely cooperative and had volunteered to respond in any location he was requested. The coroner, Dr. Richard E. Olney, was living proof of the old adage "you can't tell a book by its cover." The crime lab unit personnel could still recall the first time he appeared to testify in a homicide trial. He was short, about 5'7" in height, with thinning gray hair, usually in a crew type cut, and he looked older than his years. He had a tendency to walk with head slightly bowed, back slightly bent, in almost a stooped posture. He also usually wore suits that looked wrinkled and didn't seem to fit well. It could be said that he didn't make a great first impression. However, under that suit was the extremely fit body of a former college wrestler. And, he had a voice that contrasted widely with his appearance. Personnel still remember him taking the stand and having the defense attorney look at him with disbelief – you could read the attorney's mind processing the thought "this is the famous pathologist, Richard Olney?" But then the prosecuting attorney asked him for his name for the record, and he replied "Richard E. Olney" in a voice so resonant and powerful that witnesses swear the courtroom chandelier actually swayed from the force! In a number of cases during this era, his work, opinions and testimony lived up to his reputation.

The Grave

Coroner Olney, upon his arrival, assisted the crime lab crew in carefully excavating the grave. In addition to trace evidence such as hairs and fibers, the searchers were cognizant that a shovel used to dig the slopes of the grave, might leave behind sufficient toolmarks for identification of the blade defects. (This particular crew had, in fact, identified a shovel with markings in the soil in the murder of a State Police Trooper only a few years before.) However, this soil was too dry and crumbly to display adequate markings from defects in the tip of the blade. After the lengthy excavation process, coupled with appropriate measurements and photographs, and retrieval of potential trace evidence, the body was removed. The grave was found to be about 4-5' deep, about 3' wide, and 6' long. It was nearly as large as a professional site.

The victim was a heavy set white male, probably in his 40s, and dressed in a nice business suit. Dr. Olney pointed out an apparent entrance bullet hole in the throat, just under the chin, with an apparent exit in the back of the lower head just into the hairline. He suggested the victim was walked into the area, shot at the site with the bullet possibly traversing the brain stem and disappearing. From the conditions at the site, he theorized the victim was probably standing, facing the footpath when the shot was fired and that he fell prostrate immediately on his back, creating the blood spatter on leaves as his head struck the ground.

Using this theory, the searchers attempted to find a spent cartridge case, in the event a repeating or semi-automatic firearm was involved. Assuming the more likely trajectory of an ejected case, they crawled on hands and knees, moving grass, twigs, and leaves as they moved to a spot about 9-10' right of the possible shooter's position. One searcher, to his amazement, discovered a shiny, fresh, .380 Auto. caliber fired cartridge case.

III

The Solution

The body was removed to the nearby city morgue. As investigators checked with the police, a report came in about a local businessman, George Dumas, who had just been reported as missing. It seemed he had left home that morning to drive to his business some miles away, but never arrived. After some time lapse, an employee had called his home to check on him. Eventually his wife called to report her husband as possibly missing. The description matched the victim and it was quickly confirmed that they were one and the same.

An all points bulletin was issued for regional police to be on the lookout for Dumas's missing car. Not long after, a city cruiser radioed that they had located it parked on a side street in the business district. The car was safe guarded and then towed into the city garage. The vehicle was placed in a chained off area, marked with evidence ribbon. Later, the crime scene crew arrived to search the car. This part of the crime scene search was headed by "Black Dan" Moore and Paul Brandon of the Latent Print Unit of the State Crime laboratory. It could be safely said that these two dedicated officers were responsible for the critical physical evidence "breaks" in more homicide cases than any others in state history.

The officers, after preliminary notes and photographs, began a meticulous search of the car. Their primary area of responsibility was that of latent or hidden fingerprints, although, the need for undisturbed trace evidence, hair, fibers, blood, etc., must always be borne in mind. They were somewhat surprised by the condition of the car interior. Every inside surface, that a criminal might touch in his travels, showed unmistakable signs of having been wiped clean with a soft cloth. That is, with one exception. Although the steering wheel appeared shiny clean, latent print powder developed a rather fresh, pronounced partial palm print at about the 12 o'clock position, mostly on the back portion of the wheel. The print was photographed with print camera using a 1:1 Nikon lens. It was then carefully lifted with print tape and mounted on a transparent backer. For all practical purposes, this was the only associated evidence of real value that was recovered.

Meanwhile, detectives were busy trying to develop leads. Early on they learned that George Dumas, the victim, had been married a short time to his wife Florence, or Flo as she was known, a much younger woman. Business acquaintances and friends described the relationship as a stormy one. There was a rumor that Flo had married him for his money. It was also learned that she had a brother with a criminal record who was now working at a large plant in the City.

One of the early leads to check out was the brother-in-law. However, detectives learned that he had been at work on the day in question and according to the clock data there was insufficient time for him to have accosted the victim, driven to the burial site, dug a grave, and returned to the city in time to punch in. Apparently, he could be excluded.

In the meantime, the latent print examiners assured the investigators that the partial palm print was likely to be that of the killer and that it contained sufficient ridge detail to identify the person. They requested the officers to obtain known inked palm impressions from any potential suspects for comparison. Routine investigation revealed that the victim was acquainted with a number of lower level "Mafia" types, mainly through participation in the "numbers" gambling business out of his store. The officers assembled a list of possibilities and began to obtain and provide known inked finger and palm prints for elimination. Included in one delivery was a set of such impressions from the brother-in-law, Richard Burzynski.

Back at the crime lab, the latent print analysts were routinely comparing the known impressions when suddenly Paul Brandon pounded his desk and exclaimed "damn it, we've got him!" When things settled down, Paul pointed out a number of ridge structures with the same features and exact location as those found in the evidence print from the steering wheel. Paul and Dan excitedly called the Sheriff's Office to report on the "make." However, the chief investigator advised they had better double check the identification as the time line prevented Burzynski from being involved. "Black Dan," the section leader, assured the detective that IDs were always double checked and he had better check his time line.

Burzynski was picked up and advised of his Miranda rights to an attorney and that he need not talk to the officers, etc. He advised he knew his rights, but they were wasting their time, as he had no knowledge of the crime. He further told them to check out his work schedule and they would learn that he was working when the crime occurred. During the interview, he was asked if he had ever used the victim's car. He quickly exclaimed, "Hell no, he wouldn't give me the time of day."

Finally, the detectives decided to go for broke and they advised him they had a positive make of his palm print which would prove he had recently drove the car. He blurted out "that's impossible." When they asked him why that was impossible, he stammered, "I've just never driven that car." The chief detective then gambled and asked "It's not because you forgot to wipe it clean, is it?" Richard clenched his teeth and blurted out "Oh _____, damn that bitch!"

Burzynski then told how, on the return trip to town, he had stopped in a secluded spot near the City limits and wiped all the door handles, door edges, rear view mirror, steering wheel, dashboard, etc. so that there would be no fingerprints. He then drove to the place where he abandoned the car by placing his shirt-cuffed wrists against the bottom of the steering wheel to control the car movements. He had forgotten that a woman pulled out of a gas station driveway and he had to grab for the top of the wheel in order to swerve out of her path!

Now the investigators were curious about how he managed to juggle the time on the time clock. He hadn't really done that. He had carefully planned to do away with his brother-in-law to help his sister out. He knew that George Dumas always left early to open his business and the route he followed. He called George a day earlier and asked him for a lift downtown, arranging to be picked up at a certain corner. He then borrowed his sister's car, took a shovel from the garage, drove to the burial site and prepared the grave in advance!

The following morning George picked him up as promised and he commandeered the car, drove to the gravesite, walked George to the spot, shot him and dropped him in the hole. He then quickly covered the body and spread leaves about. He returned to the city as previously described. On the way, he discarded the pistol. After abandoning the car, he took the city bus to work and punched in on time!

Obviously, without the partial palm print, this case may have been extremely difficult to solve.

THE KIDNAPPER AND THE BROOCH

I

The Kidnapping

Nora Clark and her best friend, Sarah Howe, were finally on their way out of church. Nora had stayed after Mass to show Father John her infant daughter, Sabrina, and to make arrangements for the child's upcoming baptism. By this time the church parking lot, about a half mile from the University, was cleared of cars and people. The rain clouds had dissipated and now the sun was fast turning Sunday into a rather warm, muggy afternoon. Sarah was driving her late model car and headed for the driver's door. Seemingly, out of nowhere, a rather scruffy looking young man appeared. Sarah was shocked to see a black pistol in his hand, to see that it was pointed directly at her chest, and to hear him order Nora and her into the car at gunpoint.

The stranger directed Sarah to drive, Nora and the baby to take the front passenger seat, and he sat behind Sarah in the rear seat. The women looked helplessly through the parking lot and up and down the street. To their astonishment, there was not a living human being in sight, although they were in town and close by the University. Sarah drove away as directed, turned onto the main road out-of-town, and onto the nearby state highway. Within a matter of minutes, they had effectively vanished.

After several turns, Sarah found herself driving on a narrow, winding secondary road, composed of numerous sharp curves and hills. She became vaguely aware that they were seeing less and less of civilization and proceeding into one of the more desolate areas in this region. During the trip, thus far, their kidnapper talked incessantly in a somewhat rambling fashion as he waved the pistol around in a threatening manner.

By this time, Sarah was convinced that the stranger was a real "nut-case" and that there was a real likelihood that she, Nora, and the baby, might not live much longer. She decided that she had to do something – she was aware, of course, that Nora was restricted to the care of her infant daughter. At this point, the roadway was extremely curvy and she slowed deliberately, advising that she was afraid of the S curves ahead. In the middle of one bad curve, she suddenly opened the driver's door, let go of the wheel, and rolled out of the car, rolling over and over until she had disappeared in a ditch on the left side of the road. As she glanced down the road, she could see the armed stranger had grabbed the wheel, had straightened out the path of the car, and was apparently climbing over the seat into the front of the vehicle.

Sarah clambered out of the ditch, noting quickly that she apparently had no broken bones, only road and gravel burns and bruises. She began to run down a fence line, through a woods and farmer's field until she could run no further. What a relief it was to spot a farmhouse with signs of life.

Sarah had no difficulty in attracting the attention of the farmer's wife from the house and, in short order, her husband from the barn. As soon as they could get her slightly calmed down, the wife ministered to her scrapes and bruises while the husband made notes regarding the vehicle and the armed kidnapper. Then a call was placed to the County Sheriff's Office and from there to the State Police Operations Center where an "All Points Bulletin" was broadcast on the various radio frequencies for all police units to be on the lookout for the car, the kidnapper, and the hostages. In addition, the State Police helicopter and single engine Cessna were put on aerial search status.

Meanwhile, the deranged gunman had driven the car some distance away and down a small side road. At a location, where the terrain was extremely brushy and wooded, he suddenly wrenched the wheel and drove tangentially off the road, through the underbrush and small sapling trees. The car bounced and crashed along until it stopped, for all practical purposes, buried in a canopy of brush and trees, unseen from roadway or air.

Nora was pulled screaming from the vehicle, while her baby daughter was left lying on the front floorboard of the car. The kidnapper advised her not to struggle or he would shoot her and the baby. After a brief moment, she was thrown to the ground, partially disrobed, and violently raped! At this time, the would-be killer reneged on his promise not to harm her and the child. The baby was left lying on the floor of the front passenger area of the vehicle and Nora was jerked and dragged to the rear of the vehicle. Here the gunman opened the trunk, pushed Nora inside, slammed the trunk lid shut in a closed locked position. By this time of day, the sun was extremely hot, the air was quite humid, and the inside of the trunk felt like an oven.

*Fig 22 – Car trail plowed through the brush.

*Fig. 23 – Victim's car in the woods.

For a few moments, Nora was panic stricken, but she felt some relief to hear the kidnapper apparently run through the brush and away from the car's location. She reflected, for a brief period on the events of the day, only realizing that she and the baby might not be found for some time and both would surely die inside of the car. She had to do something and she did!

Nora was quite petite, just over 5 feet tall, and probably weighing less than one hundred pounds. She had always secretly prided herself on being in top physical condition and strong for her size. On this day, she was wearing strap sandals with hard leather soles and she began to ram the soles against the back of the rear seat and springs. She repeated this action, over and over, and finally saw light streaming through a gap she had created on one side. No matter how her feet hurt or how tired she was, she kept it up until the gap was large enough for her to slither through into the rear seat area and then out of the car. She grabbed the baby and took off running back down the tracks left in the brush and toward the road.

The Kidnapper

From the first moment in the Church parking lot, their abductor was weird. At times, he appeared to be very nervous, while at other times he seemed to be in a daze. At no time did he tell his victims why he had taken them at gunpoint. The only consistent thing was that he liked to talk.

The one topic that alarmed Sarah and Nora was that he talked a lot about his personal life. They couldn't help but wonder why he would give up so much detail, unless, perhaps, he intended to kill them, making such remarks meaningless. After Sarah rolled out of the car, Nora was left to decipher his ramblings. She made a mental note to try to remember what she could in order to attempt identification of their kidnapper.

During the ride, he mentioned that he was married and was the father of three children! He stated further that he lived in a major city, just a short distance from the University. Nora judged him to be in his mid-twenties, about 5'10" tall, of medium build, fair completed, and with brown curly hair. She made a special mental note of his footwear, apparently near new, shiny black loafers.

Initially, Nora had begun to believe that this was a mixed-up and slightly deranged individual, who may not intend her any harm. That is, until he drove the car off into the brush and assaulted her. That part had been a rude shock and a chilling eye opener to her. Now, she could only believe he was a violent criminal with a con-artist mentality. But now, she and the baby were still alive, no thanks to him, and they had to find help.

Nora found her way out of the brush and ran breathlessly down the narrow road wondering if anyone lived in this area. But then she heard the rumbling of a powerful engine and a large logging truck came around the next bend. The trucker stopped to see what was wrong with the young woman with the infant. In short order, he had contacted his radio dispatcher and advised him of the situation. The dispatcher immediately contacted the Sheriff's Office and the State Police.

The K-9

The abductor had made his way cross-country and through the margins of several large farms. He had been running part of the way and was tired and winded. He wasn't sure whether any of his victims were alive and capable of setting the police on his trail. When Sarah rolled out of the car many miles ago, he caught sight of her body rolling across the highway out of the corner of his eye. He was too busy gaining control of the careening vehicle to ascertain whether she was capable of rising to her feet. His glances at the rear view mirror were of no help in this regard. As for Nora, she was securely locked in the trunk of the abandoned car and would probably not be found alive.

He was crossing a huge field of wheat, when he heard the unmistakable sound of a nearby helicopter. He immediately threw himself, flattened and face down on the ground and vegetation. Assuming the chopper could be police manned, his instincts were to make himself less visible. His assumption was correct as the blade noise came from the State Police helicopter.

The chopper pilot was accompanied by a trooper and his K-9 German Shepard. The officers were experienced in aerial search and their sharp eyes quickly picked up the out-of-synch outline of the kidnapper, lying motionless in the field. The pilot circled and assumed a hovering position nearby, then lowered the trooper and his dog. As soon as they hit the ground, they headed directly toward the criminal. The gunman, still holding the pistol in his right hand, raised himself up on one elbow in order to get a clear shot at the officer. But then, he caught sight and sound of the enraged and snarling K-9 as he heard a warning from the trooper. The kidnapper let out a moan and threw the pistol several feet away. The officer searched him, handcuffed him with his wrists restrained behind his back, and recovered the thrown pistol. So ended the terrifying abduction of two very gritty and intelligent young women and a baby.

IV

The Crime Scene Connection

Subsequent to the arrest and discovery of the abandoned car, the State Crime Laboratory was requested to send a crew to search the crime scene. The area around the vehicle was carefully searched for any "trace" evidence that might relate to the victims and/or their abductor. At the conclusion of that search the car was towed to the nearest State Police garage where the vehicle, a major part of the crime scene, was meticulously searched for evidence.

A number of partial finger and palm prints were found, dusted, photographed, and lifted for comparison. In addition, certain trace items were located, confiscated, and safeguarded in sealed packets for potential future comparison. Many years ago, a famous forensic scientist named Locard, pointed out that when a criminal commits a crime, he invariably leaves "trace" evidence, a term for small and sometimes microscopic matter, from himself at the scene and takes with him trace evidence that originated from the scene. Such trace evidence may include hairs and fibers, body fluids like blood and semen, soil, bits of broken wood, glass, or plastic, traces of concrete or asphalt, flower or weed parts, clothing impressions, and almost anything that may connect the criminal and the scene of the crime.

Even today, this Theory is often referred to as "Locard's Exchange Principle."

However, in this case, a different form of evidence was discovered and photographically recorded. This evidence both surprised and astounded investigators and crime scene searchers alike.

Nora, while locked in the trunk of the car, felt she would be unable to get out and would probably die there. She also had no way of knowing whether or not Sarah had survived her dive from the moving vehicle. As she lay in the car trunk, she removed a decorative brooch from her dress and opened the clasp. Using the point of the pin, she scratched the following information in a recessed area on the underside of the trunk lid:

B CURLY HAIR
FATHER 3
20-25
M BUILD
LANSING
BL LOAFERS

These markings were not that easy to find and see. It required a searcher to physically assume a position below the lid and the use of side lighting to clearly make out the inscriptions. The young mother had left behind this detail to assist in identification of the culprit even after her expected death.

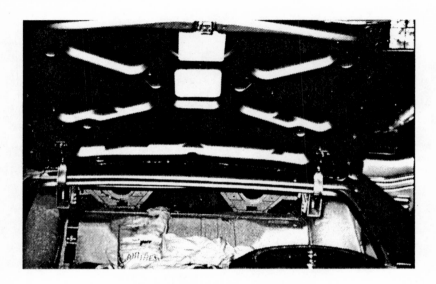

*Fig. 24 – Underside of car trunk lid.

*Fig. 25 – Close-up photograph of markings on the underside
of the trunk lid.

The author was involved in the search and subsequent recording of this unusual evidence. For many years afterward, this case and photographs of this evidence were used in crime scene search seminars to emphasize the proper search of a car trunk where a victim may have been transported therein. As the slide photos were shown, students would be asked, "how many of you would have found this crucial evidence?" Invariably, there would be no response. They would then be reminded that the author, of course, had done so. This would usually provoke a distasteful reaction from the class toward their pompous instructor until they remembered or were reminded that the victim had lived in this case.

At that point, it would be admitted that these crucial markings would probably have been missed without the assistance of the victim! One thing is certain, those crime scene students would never search the trunk of a car without looking under the lid and in any other accessible places for markings left by a crime victim!

THE "THRILL KILLER" AND

CIRCUMSTANTIAL EVIDENCE

I

The Senseless Crime

At the top of the list of crimes difficult to solve are murders committed by a "thrill seeker," i.e., a lone individual who kills only to see how it feels, without apparent motive, and where the victim is unknown to the killer and picked at random. Such was the case that faced the State Police some years ago. It was a senseless crime, without apparent motive, and involved the killing of an innocent teenage boy. The victim was well liked in the small Northern community and had no history of problems with the law.

On a pretty Spring day, Charlie Munson, age 16, walked the main road out of the village to it's T intersection with County Road 926. At this point, he stopped and waited for his good friend Al Bergland, to pick him up. Al was like an older brother and on this day he had arranged to pick Charlie up on his travel through town and was to take him along on a trout fishing trip into the National Forest.

Charlie checked his watch and decided he would have some time to kill before Al showed. At the intersection, there was an empty sand or salt barrel, sitting upside down on the curb, just off the roadway. Charlie decided to sit on the barrel while he waited.

A short time later, "Big John" Tiensivu drove his heavy dump truck down the main roadway and made a left turn North up Co. Rd. 926. As he was slowing and completing his turn, he noticed Charlie sitting on the barrel, waving at him. As he straightened out to proceed on #926 he waved out the window and glanced up at his rear view mirror.

Directly behind Charlie Munson was a dense stand of timber that came within about 100 ft. of the boy. Big John noticed the figure of a man, standing at the edge of the trees. Probably another one of those naturalist/tourist types he thought amusingly as he disappeared out of sight.

At the appointed hour, Al Bergland drove to the intersection and looked diligently for Charlie Munson to no avail. Perhaps, he thought, Charlie may have been delayed and since he lived only about a mile away, Al drove to the home to see what was keeping Charlie. But, at the home, the boy's mother explained she hadn't seen him since he left earlier in order to meet Al at the intersection.

Al checked at the local main street service station and the owner advised he had seen Charlie walk, much earlier, apparently in-route to the intersection. Now, Al drove back to the corner and parked. He walked back to the area and looked down both roads but there still was no sign of Charlie. At this time, he was standing alongside the upturned barrel. As he gazed around, somewhat puzzled, he noticed what appeared to be a rather large disturbed area of sand behind the barrel. From this area, he observed what looked like two irregular, close together, tracks leading through the tall grass and into high weeds and brush between the woods and the intersection.

Al followed these "tracks" a short distance and stopped abruptly as he came across his young friend. The boy was lying on his back, face up, and did not appear to be breathing. Al scrambled out of the weeds and went for help. This began an extensive police investigation and later a sensational trial, unseen in this rural small town community ever before.

II

The Crime Scene and the Physical Evidence

State Police troopers from a nearby post responded, followed by crime scene personnel from the state crime laboratory, and ultimately by detectives from headquarters. Initially, the area at and near the body was carefully scrutinized for any possible evidence. It was determined that Charlie fell backwards off the barrel and was probably unconscious when he struck the ground. He was then partly picked up by the upper torso and dragged backwards to his final resting place. It seemed obvious that he had suffered some type of trauma that caused immediate incapacitation. Early examination of the victim revealed only a slightly matted hair area in the back of his head, probably the result of dried blood, indicating the likelihood of a small caliber gunshot.

The first officers protected the scene and turned it over to crime scene personnel. In this case, like many others, this action saved the day by preserving the all important fragile evidence that followed.

Scene searchers were able to locate fragmentary and partial footwear impressions of a boot type pattern in the sandy areas, interspersed among the weeds. These tracks were traced from near the sand barrel to inside the woods and to a narrow trail of two ruts in the sand that paralleled the main roadway. On this trail-road they observed fresh partial tire tracks leaving the area and the boot-prints seemed to culminate at the trail-road where a vehicle had been parked.

The searchers also pinpointed a location where a person had posted near the edge of the woods and where similar boot prints were noted. Apparently this individual was a heavy smoker as several Kool cigarette butts, fresh in appearance, were located in this spot. They were measured, photographed and carefully collected.

Investigators were convinced that the perpetrator of this crime had stood near the edge of the forest for some time, probably watching Charlie Munson sitting on the sand barrel about 100 ft. away. The responsible party must have stealthily approached the victim from the rear, shot him in the back of the head without warning, and then dragged him off!

The partial boot prints displayed size and general pattern, but due to the dried, loose, sandy nature of the soil, there did not seem to be much chance for distinguishing unique characteristics to allow for positive identification of the footwear. However, there was one repeated phenomena that caught the searchers attention, and subsequent close-up photography. Adjacent to the partial boot prints, there were a number of scooped out indentations in the soil. Apparently, they were produced by the toe of the right boot leading to a theory that the culprit might be "gimpy" or have a defect in his right foot or leg.

The partial tire impressions were not of much greater value, but close-up photos and plaster casts were made of several apparently created by the rear or drive tires. It was also observed that the front tires were of a common passenger tire, while the rear tires were apparently "knobbies" or mud/snow tires. These rear tires appeared to display a few individual characteristics such as cuts, or small breaks in the lugs, etc. Of course, damage and wear may allow for positive identification of the tires.

Later, an autopsy confirmed that the victim had been shot once, apparently at close range, in the back of the head. The bullet recovered from his brain was a badly mutilated .22 long rifle caliber lead bullet. It's condition is often seen with lead bullets from head shots, that is, mushroomed, torn, smashed, with fragments missing. However, sufficient land and groove impressions remained to measure class characteristics. Crime laboratory examination of the bullet revealed rifling class characteristics known to exist on only a small number of firearms manufacturers' products at this time. At the head of this short list were .22 LR caliber revolvers, manufactured by Smith and Wesson, and the investigators were so advised.

The Investigation

While officers were still searching the scene, "Big John", the truck driver, came back from his haul and stopped to inquire as to what was happening. He was shocked to hear about the young fellow. While talking to one of the troopers, he quickly volunteered that he had some information of possible value. He went on to recite how he had turned at the intersection that morning, waved to the victim, and noticed a stranger at the edge of the woods, in his rear-view mirrors. This information immediately grabbed the officers' attention. Their first question, of course, was "Can you identify him?" Of course, he couldn't, as it was a long distance and in the mirror. But, he could offer some help. "Big John" told them "it was a white man, he was wearing a white T shirt, he appeared to have short hair, and he had some object on a rope or cord hanging around his neck." "Big John" also advised that the man was of about average height and build. He apologized for not being able to tell them more, but the officers assured him they were extremely grateful for what he provided.

By this time, a cordon of officers had arrived to assist, and were given specific assignments. First, they were briefed on what was now known and the lug type tire tracks and boot tracks were described in detail. The mud/snow tires were very popular in this part of the state and the troopers knew them well.

They were then dispatched in the three directions from the fatal intersection, i.e., east and west on the main road and north on #926. They were ordered to check every side road and trail that led off the roadways in the event the criminal might be staying in any of the local tourist or vacation cabins, of which there are many in this part of the state.

The troopers went about this task diligently and one, only about five or six miles out of town, excitedly radioed that he had discovered similar fresh tracks leading off on a dirt trail road. He paused to await backup and then several officers followed the tracks several miles to a clearing with a small frame cabin.

In the parking area was a late model full-size station wagon with tires of a similar pattern to the crime scene impressions. As the officers approached the car, they observed an opened package of Kool cigarettes on the dashboard and a pair of small binoculars on a leather neck-strap lying on the front seat. In a brief moment they were approached by the cabin owner, Clifford Brantley, who engaged them in a brief conversation. Brantley was white, about medium height and weight, with light brown hair in a crew cut, and he was wearing a white T shirt! After a short interview, Clifford Brantley was arrested and taken into custody for the murder of Charlie Munson. Although Brantley denied any knowledge of the crime, the match with Tiensivu's description, the Kool cigarettes, the binoculars on a leather neck strap, the fresh tire tracks to the cabin, convinced arresting officers to take him in. It should be remembered that this was a remote area of the state with a small population.

IV

The Facts and the Alibis

Although there appeared to be sufficient circumstantial evidence, there were no positive identifications of any kind, either by personal eyewitness or physical evidence. Needless to say, the suspect denied any knowledge of the crime and asserted his innocence.

When detectives asked Clifford about the "identification" by the truck driver, Brantley replied, "it's not possible, and besides, how many white men have short hair and wear white T shirts?"

When asked about the binoculars on the neck-strap, he simply inquired, "how many naturalists, rangers, tourists, bird watchers, etc. have such an accessory?"

When asked about the Kool cigarettes, his answer, not surprisingly, was that "there must be thousands or possibly hundreds of thousands of people who smoke Kools."

However, officers felt they had a better chance to tie him to the crime scene with tire and boot impressions. The rear tires had been removed from his station wagon and submitted to the Crime Laboratory. Examination of these tires revealed a number of glaring defects that should have been seen in the evidence tracks, but weren't.

The Laboratory analysts reported to the detectives that most of these defects appeared as if they had been recently cut and material removed with a sharp instrument. If Clifford was the killer, they felt he had deliberately altered the tires to defeat attempts at identification! But, Clifford Brantley had a ready answer for this assertion. On the fatal day, he had gone trout fishing on a remote stream and had gotten the car stuck trying to ford a small creek. Further, he had to rock it back and forth, spinning the rear-drive wheels, to get out of there. The creek bed was loaded with small sharp stones, according to Brantley, and they must be what caused the fresh damage to the tires!

The next item to be resolved was the boot imprints. Diligent investigation discovered the peculiar imprints were to be found on military surplus "combat jungle boots." They then got their first break on the physical evidence. They learned that the suspect had a close friend in the vicinity, Joe Shanakit, a member of the local Indian tribe and sometime fishing and hunting guide for visiting sportsmen. They learned that Joe had been seen wearing jungle boots on several occasions. When they located him, he produced his boots. They were of the same size and pattern as the imprints seen at the crime scene. Joe further advised that Mr. Brantley had purchased two pairs of the combat jungle boots at a military surplus store in the Southern part of the State where his permanent home was located. He and Brantley wore the same size and Clifford had given him one pair.

Armed with the information from Joe Shanakit, the detectives confronted Brantley. He stated that on the fatal morning he had been trout fishing and when trying to get his car out of the creek bed, his boots became soggy wet and muddy. On the trip back to the cabin, he hung the boots on the radio antenna to dry out.

Apparently, while traversing the brushy wilderness, they must have been torn off the car but not discovered until he was back at the cabin. Therefore, he has no idea where they are now.

The next possible connection was the firearms evidence. The Crime Laboratory was advised that the detectives had learned that Clifford Brantley was a "gun nut." In the State, handguns must be registered and it was discovered that Brantley had sixteen registered firearms. A search warrant was executed on his Southern home and fifteen weapons were found and checked. Only one firearm was missing. The officers were not surprised to learn the missing firearm was a .22 LR caliber Smith & Wesson revolver, the "kit gun" model, so called, as it is small and easily carried in a hiker's kit bag.

How was Brantley going to explain this one? Well, he didn't disappoint the officers as he had a ready answer. He advised that several weeks, before the day of the murder, he had gone trout fishing on a small soggy bottom, spring-filled lake, one of many in the area. Natives called them "bottomless" because of their silty and swamp-like nature. On this trip, he used a canoe to have access to the lake. He carried his .22 LR S&W revolver tucked into his waistband. A large brook trout took his bait and engaged him in a contest. He was standing during the fight, lost his balance, and the canoe tipped over. By the time he had righted the canoe and made his way to shore, he found the revolver was missing, apparently lost in the lake bottom. State Police skin divers, with the assistance of large magnets, attempted recovery of the weapon to no avail. Due to the conditions of the lake and depth of the water, they could not state definitely that the weapon could not be there!

Finally, attempts to show any relationship between the suspect and the victim were unsuccessful. As far as the officers knew, they had never been acquainted. It was, as it seemed, a thrill killing by a loner who had no criminal record and was only considered to be reclusive.

The Trial

Now the question was, would a jury believe in all these excuses, or taken together, would they be sufficient for connection? The local Prosecuting Attorney was convinced that Clifford Brantley was guilty. He agreed to try him for the murder of Charlie Munson but requested assistance from the State's Attorney General.

Shortly before the trial was to commence, the Attorney General sent a lawyer from his staff to assist. Asst. AG Greg Stewart, at first sight, was not an impressive man. He was slight of build, short, with wisps of thinning gray hair and wearing wire rimmed glasses. However, when he spoke, all that changed. He had been a Prosecutor for many years and his strong voice and positive demeanor exuded confidence. The County Prosecutor and lead detectives felt the Attorney General had made a wise choice.

The Prosecutor opened with statements to the jury emphasizing the fact that Clifford Brantley had no real alibi that could be confirmed. He ticked off each item of circumstantial evidence, emphasizing over and over that the defendant had no plausible answers. The defense attorney, an experienced trial lawyer from down State, pointed out in his opening statement that Brantley had steadfastly maintained his innocence and a string of "coincidences" could not and should not be used to convict a man of murder.

As Jeffrey Smith, the prosecutor, introduced his first witnesses, he emphasized the "coincidences" one by one. After establishing the body of the crime (the corpus-delecti), he brought to the stand crime scene investigators to establish the nature of the scene; the fresh Kool cigarette butts at the posting site, the tire tracks on the sandy trail, the drag marks and the boot prints, and especially the right boot impression with the attendant scuff or drag marks. He next introduced the rear tires from the car and the spare boots obtained from Joe Shanakit, the defendant's friend.

Finally, the defense had its' turn and the attorney called the defendant to testify in his own behalf. One by one he attacked the circumstantial evidence and explained them away as he had to the police investigators. He emphasized the defendant had always stated he was innocent and has not changed his story.

Then, it was time for cross-examination. The Prosecutor and Assistant Attorney General had decided before hand on a definite plan. The two brought into the courtroom an easel and placed upon it an enlarged map of the county mounted on hardboard. The prosecutor then advised the defendant that he had a series of questions about his exact travels during his alibi fishing trip. He then handed the defendant a pointer and asked him to walk across the courtroom to the easel. As Clifford Brantley arose from the witness chair to begin his journey across the room, Prosecutor Smith and Asst. AG Stewart simultaneously arose halfway out of their chairs, staring intently at the feet of the defendant. The jury immediately followed this cue and followed the legs and feet of Brantley. The eerie silence of the courtroom was broken only by a series of shuffling sounds as the defendant dragged his right shoe toe area on the floor with nearly every step. At that instant, the descriptions and photographs of the scuff mark evidence, made by a right boot, flashed through the minds of everyone in the courtroom.

For all practical purposes, the trial was over. Nothing else that was said could pull this vision from the minds of the jurors. They were out less than one day and returned a verdict of guilty of Murder in the 1st Degree.

FACTS AREN'T ALWAYS FACTUAL — THE TRILOGY

Introduction

In the history and drama of firearms identification, much space is devoted to the process of bullet and cartridge case identification; i.e., comparison of such evidence with a suspected firearm. Needless to say, in most cases involving such comparisons, a capital crime is involved, often murder. However, there are numerous other important tasks that a well-trained and experienced analyst must perform, such as determination of bullet pathways, trajectories and deflections, distance of discharge, firearm condition and safety elements. Much of this needed analysis goes toward the reconstruction of shooting events, hopefully to assist in answering the question of how did the shooting occur, rather than what person or firearm is involved.

The accurate determination of how these events occurred — if they were accidental, suicide or murder, negligent in nature — is often a difficult task. The following three, very simple, examples may illustrate this difficulty.

The Hunter

In Southern Michigan, on a sunny October day, Richard Canfield was beating a path through a farmer friend's weed field when he flushed a "rooster" pheasant. He mounted his 12-gauge double and fired. Feathers flew and the bird swerved momentarily then straightened and soared across the fence line dropping into the neighboring farmer's cornfield. The hunter crawled over the fence and proceeded to search for the wounded pheasant.

In the meantime, the owner of the cornfield, Henry Jacobs, had heard the nearby gun discharge and came out of his barn in time to see Canfield cross the fence line. He yelled at the hunter to get out of his corn but Canfield either didn't hear him or ignored his demands. Richard Canfield was apparently unaware of the local reputation of the farmer. Henry Jacobs was rumored to hate hunters and trespassers and reportedly had fired a scare shot near at least one.

At this time, Henry Jacobs returned to the barn and retrieved his loaded, rusted, single-shot, bolt-action .22LR caliber rifle off a peg on the barn wall. He stepped outside the barn door and viewed Canfield still moving down his corn rows. He raised the rifle and fired one shot. Canfield let out a cry and collapsed in the corn. Henry ran to him, quickly examined the victim and then ran back to the farmhouse to call the paramedics. Richard Canfield, it turned out, was extremely lucky, with the .22 caliber bullet lodged next to his spinal column. He lived and eventually recovered fully. The bullet had struck him in the mid-back, nearly dead center. Doctors advised that Canfield would have been paralyzed, at the least, if the bullet had been about 1" to the right of its point of impact.

As a result of this event, a formal complaint was lodged against Henry Jacobs. He was arrested and charged with "attempted murder." As part of the investigation, the bullet and rifle were submitted to the State Crime Laboratory. It was rather easy to confirm that the bullet from Canfield had been fired from Jacob's rifle. However, in examining the firearm, prior to test firing, it was noted that it did not appear to be in very good condition and the rear sight elevator was missing, thereby providing an inaccurate sight picture.

A brief interview with the investigating officer revealed that Jacobs had claimed he fired over the hunter's head by a couple of feet, strictly as a warning. The officer further advised that he paced the distance at about 200 yards. With this information in mind, accuracy tests were conducted with the rifle. It was determined that the standard velocity .22LR bullet would strike the target about 4 – 4 ½ feet below the point of aim.

Prior to trial, Henry Jacobs waived a jury and requested trial by the Circuit Judge. During the trial, I was called to testify and to describe the comparison tests of the bullet and rifle by standard comparative microscopy. The accuracy tests at the 200-yard distance and the results of these tests were also mentioned.

The defense attorney then asked for a brief recess and consultation between the attorneys, the judge, and the defendant. They met in the judge's chambers and emerged to announce that the defendant had agreed to plead guilty to a lesser charge; that of "Careless Use of a Firearm Resulting in an Injury", a Circuit Court misdemeanor, rather than the original felony charge.

I was then called into the judge's chambers and offered congratulations for taking the extra steps to conduct the accuracy tests and my forthright testimony in this regard. I left the courtroom feeling great about my testimony and the case outcome apparently based, to a large degree, on my findings.

As I walked down the courthouse corridor, I was addressed by an elderly gentleman wearing bib overalls, who advised me that he was one of Henry Jacobs neighbors. He stated that he had listened to my testimony and was quite impressed with my professionalism. He then related a brief, but interesting tale. On one occasion, he had been visiting Henry when they spotted a large hawk circling over the chicken yard. Henry went into the barn and came out with that same old, rusty, .22 caliber rifle, lifted the firearm to his shoulder, and killed that hawk in flight with one well aimed shot!

Grandpa Great

My wife's grandfather was a wiry little Canadian farmer with a wonderful grin and a wicked sense of humor. He was dearly loved by all in the family. He owned a small farm near Tilbury, Ontario, and he still tilled it by hand at age 80! The family made a trip from Central Michigan to visit "Grandpa Great", as he was affectionately called, one early winter Saturday.

We arrived early and in time for Grandpa Great to put me on one end of a two-man crosscut saw. We proceeded to cut up a large oak that had fallen on the edge of the property. We sawed until he was tired and I thought I was about to die from utter fatigue. Later, he asked me if I would like to do a little target shooting, and I said "sure." We walked out to his small barn and he took a rifle down from a spike in the inner wall. It was an old, rusted, single-shot .22LR caliber Cooey rifle with the front sight blade missing.

We walked along the field to the creek that ran along the dikes to the spillway at the pump house. "Grandpa Great" led the way out onto the dam and loaded his rifle. He handed it to me saying, "let's see what a state policeman with an expert's badge can do." The clear creek was running steadily under a thin sheet of clear ice and he pointed out a large bubble and said "let's see you hit that." I tried and missed it by a couple of feet. We reloaded and I tried again and again. I don't believe I came within a foot of the target center in several attempts.

He then took the rifle and placed the first shot through the dead center of a large fast floating bubble. I asked him, "Grandpa, how in hell can you do that with no front sight on the rifle?" He replied, "You have to learn to accommodate, son!"

III

The Killer

A few years later I was requested to examine evidence and then travel to a Southern Florida city to assist the Public Defender's Office. The case involved a juvenile from a poor neighborhood who had shot an individual and was charged with second-degree murder.

Initially firearms evidence was turned over to me for a comparison of a severely damaged .22 Long Rifle caliber bullet removed from the cranial cavity of the victim, and a "cut-down" version of a .22 LR caliber rifle from the defendant. The local crime laboratory examiner had previously made the same analysis and reported that the bullet and rifle displayed similar rifling characteristics but the bullet was too damaged for a positive identification or elimination.

The rifle was test fired to obtain specimens for the analysis. It was an old model, single-shot, with the shoulder stock and a large part of the barrel sawed-off. Of course, this meant the front sight was missing and part of the barrel was gone. Microscopic comparisons confirmed the local examiner's opinion, and the Public Defender was so advised. Later, in the PD's Office, I inquired how this crime had occurred. The public defender then provided me with a detailed description of the event. She advised that it happened late at night, in an unlighted alley, in a driving rain, when the defendant came out the back door of his mother's apartment. He had claimed that they couldn't sleep due to the noise and commotion in the alley. Allegedly, a male "pimp" with his female prostitute, was in the act of physically robbing another man. The distance from the juvenile to the victim was about 100 feet. The defendant claimed he fired one shot, over the victim's head, to scare him away. The bullet entered the victim at about the ear lobe, traveled upwards into the brain, and caused instant incapacitation and a quick death.

The attorney asked if I would be willing to go to the scene to get a better feel for the conditions. I agreed and we drove to the neighborhood. It was now getting dark and there was a steady rain that partially obscured our view. She pointed out the exact position of the shooter and his victim. We then returned to the legal office. She explained that the Prosecutor claimed that the "scare shot" was an alibi and that the investigators believed the juvenile defendant had intentionally aimed and fired this shot, delivering the bullet to the victim's head. She then asked, after testing the rifle and visiting the scene, if I had an opinion regarding the likelihood of that happening. I advised, based on the darkness, the distance, the rain storm, and the condition of the rifle, it was improbable. What she didn't hear was what I muttered half under my breath – "Even Grandpa Great couldn't make that shot!"

STRIATIONS AND THE DYING SHARK

I

The Tragedy

It was a chilly, foggy morning in North Central Florida as Robert Preston prepared to endure his early commute to work on his Kawasaki. On a nice warm sunny day, he enjoyed riding his bike to work. After all, the motorcycle got about three times the gas mileage of the average car. But, in this weather, he wished he had a second car instead.

As he traveled, the local 2-lane paved highway and rounded a curved section, he caught a fleeting glimpse of a large truck-like vehicle pulling onto the highway through the pea soup fog. He tried to swerve to avoid it, but his cycle clipped the rear corner of the vehicle. He never remembered anything of that morning from that time.

Days later, when he awoke for the first time in the hospital, he learned that he was fortunate to be alive. Some time and much pain later, he learned that he was paraplegic and would be confined to a wheelchair for life! The family vowed to find the responsible party and make him pay. To this end, they employed a highly respected law firm from the nearest city to assist in the investigation and hopefully lead a successful civil lawsuit.

The Investigation

Jeff Terwiliger, the lead attorney of the firm, agreed to take the case on a contingency basis as the Preston family had little financial assets. He first went to the Sheriff's Office and obtained a copy of the accident report and investigative file. He wasn't surprised to learn that no one had come forward to admit involvement and that the Sheriff's Office had been unable to link any individual or vehicle to the accident. In fact, as the officers knew all too well, it was entirely likely that if a large truck were involved, the driver may not have even been aware of the collision, considering the circumstances.

During a lengthy investigation, Jeff had learned that there were several companies in this region of the state that contracted with one of the country's largest and best known pulp wood processors. If one of the agents of this corporation were involved, the opportunity for a sizeable settlement was certainly present. However, interviews with company officials, drivers and helpers, only produced information relating to the activities of several truckers, who were apparently hauling logs in this area at the time of the mishap.

Jeff knew he needed some professional investigative help to track down and identify the vehicle involved. He learned of an individual,

Ed Rennert, a former forensic scientist who taught aspects of accident reconstruction at a nearby university. Rennert, at one time, was the director of a small regional crime laboratory in another part of the country.

The police, and later the victim's law firm, protected the motorcycle in the hope that trace evidence, such as paints and metal smears and toolmarks of the striking vehicle, would not be lost or destroyed. A legal chain of custody could be maintained in the event they found the responsible vehicle.

Robert Preston's Kawasaki was examined by Rennert. The "expert" pointed out an area on the fork of the motorcycle where the bright aluminum was severely abraded in a striated fashion by a harder material, such as steel. These types of markings in forensic science are typically known as striae or striated tool markings. It is generally accepted that when a hard object makes forceful contact with a softer medium, it may leave individual striated markings, which can be compared microscopically to test markings produced by the business surface of the harder material. In many cases, such a comparison can produce a conclusion of identity when utilized by an expert in toolmark identification. In other words, under ideal conditions, a vehicle might be identified as causing the toolmarks on the motorcycle. It is alleged that Rennert stated that he was one of the leading experts in this field in the United States. He further allowed that he would be cognizant of any trace evidence materials, e.g., paint smears, fabric imprints, metallic residue, etc., and, if necessary, cause any such evidence to be analyzed by an expert in trace evidence.

As the investigation progressed, Rennert advised the attorneys that he had located a trailer wheel rim from one of the logging companies. He felt it was of interest due to certain metallic smears and the types of markings and damage on the side of the wheel rim, and that it merited further study. He further stated that he had taken numerous close-up (1:1) photographic transparencies of tool markings on the motorcycle and certain markings on the wheel rim for comparison purposes.

After several contacts with the legal firm and receipt of substantial funds for his services, Rennert told the attorneys that he had been able to make a positive "match" of the wheel rim and of the motorcycle damage. He also declared that he had prepared several photomicrograph (photographs taken through the microscope) displays to illustrate this fact.

III

The Dying Shark

It was at this juncture, and more than two years after the tragic accident, that I was contacted by Lyle Jackson; a polished, intelligent, and colorful attorney from the nearby large city. He explained that he represented the defendant in this lawsuit, the "deep pockets" corporation that had leased the truck allegedly implicated. Further, he briefly related the known facts of the case and that no individual driver or truck had been identified by the police. He then advised one of the key pieces of evidence in the case revolved around Toolmark Identification and that the witness for the plaintiff had been described as one of the foremost experts in this field. He asked if I would be interested in re-examining the evidence and the opinion of the Plaintiff's expert. My reply, of course, was "you bet your life."

The toolmark evidence consisted of a series of actual size color transparencies (35mm) of striated markings around the rim of the truck trailer wheel rim and striated markings on the tube or fork of the motorcycle. The "expert" had compared the scrape markings with one another by comparing the colored slides using transmitted light and the comparison microscope. Further, several photomicrographic "matches" were produced which purported to show that the wheel rim had made forceful contact with the cycle. Attorney Jackson claimed this was a "fishing expedition" to get at the "deep pockets" of the corporation he represented. I was furnished with copies of the slides and the "matches" to re-examine. Later, I was able to examine the motorcycle and the wheel rim.

A number of technical and comparative problems were encountered with this evidence, including poor quality and mismatched photographs and slides. The images in the slides were unclear and in film so that their enlargement only made them less clear. With this type of image, there is no way to sharpen focus. I would like to emphasize a couple of significant areas of interest: the examination of the slides through the comparison microscope afforded no additional resolution or clarity of the poor quality images, only magnification of problems already existing. This is an example of what in microscopy is referred to as "empty magnification." The fuzzy and unclear images in the slides demonstrated why this is so. Also, two of the exhibits were alleged to illustrate two different "matches," i.e., correspondence of the markings at two different locations on the damaged tube (see Figs. 26-27). Review of the slide and image defects in corresponding parts of the two exhibits show clearly that they were formed by using the same markings from the very same areas. However, in Fig. 26, it can be seen that the sets of slides are flip-flopped to the other side of the hair-line divider, and one set of markings is also upside down as compared to the same markings in Fig. 27.

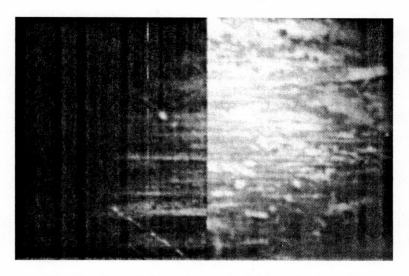

*Fig. 26—Copy of photomicrograph of slides, take through a comparison microscope; "the shark."

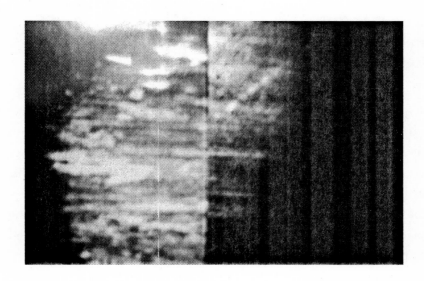

*Fig. 27—Copy of photomicrograph; "the dying shark."

In preparing for deposition and trial, I had shown these exhibits to Lyle Jackson, the company attorney. In order for him to understand the manipulation of the slides, I pointed out a rather large defect in the photomicrographs that looked like a white "blob". There can be seen a large fin shaped protrusion from this "blob" that I felt looked a good deal like a shark fin cutting the water. I felt a Florida attorney might relate to such an image. As you can see in the exhibits, in Fig. 27 the fin is upside down! Jackson laughed and said "damn it, it's a dying shark."

As a result of the re-examination of the evidence, I advised Lyle that the process used by the other "expert" was improper, and that the photo exhibits were either a sign of incompetence or a deliberate attempt to mislead interested parties.

A short time later, I was dismayed to learn that Terwiliger, the plaintiff's attorney, had allegedly contacted another expert in the field and advised Atty. Jackson that the other expert disagreed with my findings and was prepared to testify to this fact. Atty. Jackson asked me to contact this other expert, who I had known for some years, and verify this information. The "other expert" advised that he had refused to examine the evidence and had advised Terwiliger he had better rely on my opinion!

A time was then set for a sworn deposition on my part. The legal inquiry was lengthy and slightly heated at times, with two attorneys interrogating me at length. Finally, by mid-afternoon, Lyle Jackson had heard enough, and he interrupted Terwiliger. Jackson said, "that's enough Charlie, show them the dying shark." As Terwiliger and his assistant sat in disbelief, I showed them their expert's photo displays and explained how they had been manipulated to simulate matching positions. There was no match. The method used was illogical and improper. I believe the lawyers were convinced that their "expert" had conned them.

IV

The Settlement

Later, I was subpoenaed to testify at the trial. At the last minute, Atty. Jackson called to advise my testimony would not be required, as Terwiliger, the plaintiff's attorney, had withdrawn the toolmark expert and evidence from the case. Although Jackson put the information in his own inimitable style as he remarked "Charlie, the black knight and his party had just left the castle when they saw the white knight come over the hill on his white charger – they immediately retreated across the moat and drew the bridge!"

Later, Lyle advised me the trial had been continued and an out-of-court settlement had been reached. He stated something to the effect that this was a huge victory for the defendant corporation as they had agreed to only pay the plaintiff approximately $900,000 to settle. When I expressed shock at the amount of the settlement, he stated "are you kidding – can you see the jurors' faces when the plaintiff is brought into the courtroom in a wheelchair as a paraplegic, only to be opposed by the mean spirited and obviously very wealthy corporation?"

And so it goes in civil litigation, a sad testimonial to the jury system.

MURDER AND WILDFLOWERS

I

The Killings

Nancy Shepherd jumped out of the family car, beating the others into the kitchen for one of mom's oatmeal and raisin cookies and a glass of milk. It was almost a ritual on Sunday after church. The rain had stopped, the sky had cleared and it was turning out to be a beautiful afternoon. She decided to run down to Kim Martin's house and get her to go along into the State Forest to pick wildflowers. As she dashed out the door, she yelled at her mother to let her know where she was going.

Nancy and Kim were 11 and 9 years old, respectively. Their homes were only a few doors apart and comprised a small segment of this rural subdivision that bordered the state forest and lay only a few miles from the "big lake." In this area, the forest was considered a park-like wilderness, traversed by several well-worn footpaths that wound through the woods to the lake. It was late spring and the trillium, jack-in-the-pulpit, and morel mushroom grew in abundance. Nancy and Kim chose a familiar path and began their adventure.

At suppertime, Mrs. Shepherd called Kim's mother to see if the girls had returned there. The answer was negative. The two mothers went into the backyard and called loudly for the girls. There was no answer. They were a little concerned as their daughters were usually quite reliable. They asked the men, and Nancy's brothers, Tom and Joe, if they could locate them. The men split up taking separate footpaths into the forest.

After a relatively short time, Mrs. Shepherd's heart chilled as she heard Tom running through the edge of woods, screaming "Mama, Mama!" When she could get to him and calm him somewhat, he stammered "Oh God, Mama, it's Nancy and Kim." Mrs. Shepherd cried out "What is it Tommy, what about Nancy and Kim?" Tom replied, "Oh Mama, I found them; I think they're dead!"

Tom had the terrible task of leading the fathers into the woods along with a couple of troopers from the local State Police post. They found the two girls lying directly on the path, separated by about 50 feet. They were still neatly dressed in their Sunday church dresses, and with a small, scattered bouquet of wildflowers alongside each of them. Kim was the closest to the observers and was lying face down. Nancy, the furthest away, was lying face up. Both of the girls were dead.

The officers noted a small neat hole with a slight trace of blood through the dress fabric and near the center of Kim's back. It appeared that she might have been shot with a small caliber firearm. Nancy's body displayed a small apparent entrance bullet hole in her forehead, in the center. The hole was surrounded by a circular pattern of fine "dots", the type of markings described as "stippling" or "tattooing", i.e., minute particles of gunshot residue driven into the skin, an unmistakable sign of close range discharge. Later, the autopsy showed that Nancy had also been shot once in the back. The bullets recovered from their bodies were all .22 long rifle caliber. They all displayed adequate class and individual characteristics for comparison purposes and investigators were so advised.

Now the investigation of the tragic and senseless killings became the paramount duty for police officers in this region of the State. Officers noted that there was no sign of a struggle or sexual assault.

It was theorized that this could be the act of a deranged individual, possibly an older child or teenager.

Investigation and Forensics

Within a few days, several names of potential suspects were floated to the officers. One name was that of Jimmy Wilson, a 16 year old, who lived a few miles away and had previously been a person of interest to law enforcement. During the past summer, Jimmy was accused of firing a small caliber rifle over the heads of several teens playing on the sand dunes at the beach.

The officers contacted Jimmy's mother at their home and learned that her son was visiting his aunt in an adjoining state. It was of considerable interest to learn that Jimmy had left on the visit only two days after the homicides. When asked if the family had access to any .22 caliber firearms, the mother replied affirmatively and produced a Stevens semi-automatic rifle from the closet, advising that it was the property of the boy's father. She readily agreed to let the officers take the rifle for routine testing.

The rifle was delivered to the Firearms/Toolmark Section of the Crime Laboratory the following day and immediately examined and tested. Two test cartridges similar to the evidence exhibits were discharged in the rifle and the bullets recovered for comparison. The test shots were fired into a tank of water so that the fine microscopic markings on the sides of the bullet would not be damaged to any extent. The bullets were then compared to one another by using the comparison microscope, basically two low-powered microscopes connected to an optical bridge, which allows the examiner to view two objects (e.g., evidence and test bullet) side by side and at the same degree of magnification. With bullets, the striated lines on the sides, created by imperfections in the bore, are compared for similar markings and patterns. In this case, the comparison was quite straight-forward and the analyst was able to find numerous patterns of striae that displayed remarkable agreement and thus conclude the evidence bullets were fired from this rifle.

The rifle was also examined for condition, defects, safety, trigger pull pressure required to fire it, and was partially disassembled to aid in this examination.

The two girls had each been shot in the back and microscopic and chemical examination of their dresses showed no firearms residues on or in the fabric. These shots had been fired at some distance, at least beyond the range where gunshot residue would be deposited. Nancy Shepherd, however, had also been shot in the forehead between the eyes, and the skin and tissues in the area displayed a small dense pattern of lead and gunpowder residues. A series of tests were conducted using similar ammunition and the suspect's rifle at distances varying from contact (touching) out to several feet. The tests indicated the rifle muzzle was more than three feet from the girls' dresses at discharge and less than one foot from little Nancy's face when the fatal shot was fired! (See Figs. 28-29)

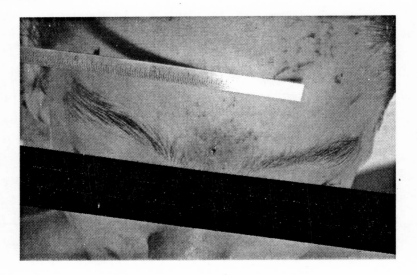

*Fig. 28 – Close-up photograph to illustrate gunshot residues.

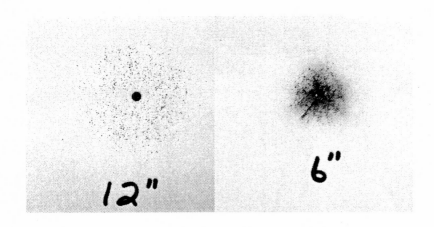

*Fig. 29 – Gunshot residue tests, discharged, 6" and 12" from
the muzzle of the firearm.

The Story

Investigators traveled to the adjoining State, obtained the assistance of city police, and went with them to the home of Jimmy Wilson's aunt. They found their suspect there and confronted him. At first, he denied any knowledge of the murders, but when advised of the identification of the rifle, he related the following story:

He stated that he tried to mislead the officers at first because he was frightened. According to Jimmy, the shootings were all a terrible accident. He stated that he had gone into the Forest that fateful day to target shoot. At one point he saw the girls on the path and called out to them. They responded and he ran to meet them. As he was running, he tripped over a log and the loaded rifle discharged as he fell to the ground. The rifle then "machine-gunned" or kept firing like an automatic weapon and he couldn't stop it until the magazine was empty.

Of course, the rifle had been thoroughly examined and tested and no such malfunction could be detected. Furthermore, Jimmy was unable to explain how the apparent final killing shot was fired into little Nancy's forehead from a distance of less than one foot!

The big question remains…why? What causes a 16 year old boy to murder two innocent little girls in this fashion?

THE WALLSINK COWBOYS

I

The Rustlers

D oc Gruber and Jerry Pitts, foreman and ranch hand respectively, were patrolling the western area of one of central Florida's largest cattle ranches. Many people think of Florida as tropical plants, citrus groves, and sandy ocean beaches. Actually, raising cattle is one of the state's top money producers. All ranchers lose a few cattle now and then, but this ranch had been plagued by cattle rustling in large numbers; apparently arranged from the inside. Doc and Jerry were following a lead in this area of the ranch. They suddenly spotted a pickup truck parked near a back fence and service road and decided to check it out. As they approached, they encountered two ranch employees, Scott Hammer and Jeff Turner, two of the names on their list of potential suspects.

As they started to question the men about their being in this location, they were surprised by Scott pulling a .357 magnum revolver from under his shirt. They were even more surprised when Scott shot them both without further discussion! Scott and Jeff loaded the bodies in the back of their pickup and proceeded to drive. Within a short distance they came upon a locked gate across the service roadway. Jeff obtained a pair of large bolt cutters from the pickup bed and cut the padlock shackle in two, opened the gate, and they continued their journey along the dirt roadway. They finally stopped at the location of the "Wallsink."

The Wallsink was one of the larger sinkholes in this part of Florida. It was quite deep and nearly filled with water. The sidewalls were nearly vertical, thus the name Wallsink. Several years before, adjoining property owners had placed a barbwire fence around the sinkhole to keep unlucky cattle or children from a watery grave. Jeff took the bolt cutters and snipped through several strands of barbwire to make a hole in the fence. He and Scott took the victims out of the pickup, slid them through the hole in the fence and down into the black waters of the Wallsink, satisfied that they would never be found.

As they were driving back to the bunkhouse, Scott remembered the Dan Wesson .357 magnum caliber revolver. He knew enough about cops and crime laboratories to know that firearms can be traced to bullets from shooting victims and he wasn't about to take that chance. On the road back, they passed a small but deep, spring fed lake. He walked to a bluff over a deep hole and threw the firearm into the water. It sank completely out-of-sight. He was satisfied it wouldn't be found.

The Investigation

It wasn't long before Gruber and Pitts and their pickup were missed. A search of the ranch revealed the missing truck in a back pasture. A few specks of blood and drag marks confirmed the worst fears. They had probably been jumped and were injured or dead somewhere. Detectives from the Sheriff's Office, after a brief investigation, and in light of the circumstances, theorized they may have come upon a couple of rustlers and proceeded along that line of investigation. In due time, they were following the same leads as the victims, and finally interviewed Jeff Turner.

The detectives asked Jeff to describe his whereabouts on the day in question, and then watched him squirm and sweat as he attempted to lie to the officers. In a relatively short span of time, they convinced the amateur criminal that he had better cooperate. They pointed out that he wouldn't want to take the fall by himself, which could lead to a trip to "Old Sparky," if he murdered the foreman and his assistant. Of course, in Florida, "Old Sparky" is well known as the electric chair used to carry out death sentences in some capital crime cases.

Jeff admitted being along on the fateful trip but stated his associate, Scott Hammer, had actually killed the two victims, even though he tried to talk him out of it. As usual, most criminals who confess in any manner try to clean up their act to a certain degree.

Next, Scott was picked up, but being a former "hard time" loser, refused to cooperate and denied it all. Jeff then took the officers and retraced the fatal trip. The investigators retrieved the cut lock shackle, several lengths of cut barbwire, and the bolt cutters from the pickup bed. Department divers descended into the Wallsink and recovered the bodies. They later recovered the revolver from the lake where Scott had dumped it. It had now been about six weeks since the crimes had taken place and the revolver was jammed and starting to corrode slightly. All of these items, along with bullets from the victims' torsos, were delivered to the Crime Laboratory for analysis. Although the officers had Jeff's admissions, they now needed corroborative physical evidence to confirm his account and put the noose around the neck of the actual shooter, his accomplice, Scott Hammer.

The Crime Laboratory

Analysts, in the Firearms and Toolmark Section, first tackled the toolmark evidence. In the meantime, the revolver was placed in an oil bath to free the action and prevent further corrosion. Examination of the lock shackle and wire ends under the stereo microscope revealed paint smears consistent with the coating on the evidence bolt cutters. Examination of the cutting and shearing surface of the bolt cutter revealed half-moon or crescent shaped smear markings in accord with the diameters of the lock shackle and wires, indicating this could very well be the right tool. Test cuts were made from the suspicious areas through lead wire of suitable diameter and these specimens were then compared to the evidence lock and wire, using the forensic comparison microscope. In this manner, striated markings (microscopic ridges and valleys) produced by imperfections in the cutting edges, could be compared side-by-side. Remarkable agreement was found in the cut markings on tests and evidence. Some of these patterns were photographed through the microscope (see Figs. 30 & 31). There was no question that this pair of bolt cutters was used to open the gate and make the fence hole at the Wallsink.

*Fig. 30 – Padlock shackle toolmark comparison; cut lock to left of divider, test markings from bolt cutter to right

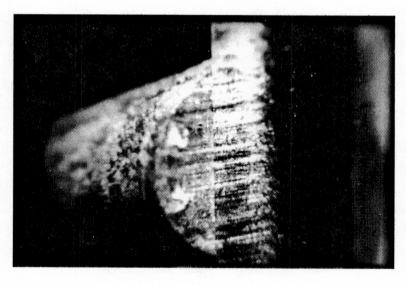

*Fig. 31 – Barb wire toolmark comparison.

The next step was to partly disassemble the revolver, clean it thoroughly, and restore the action. Particular attention was given to the barrel, which had contained considerable marl and muck. As it was cleaned, a slight amount of rust was noted near the muzzle end. However, it was surprising to see the minimum corrosion resulting from six weeks submersion. Test shots were fired, using similar ammunition. The tests were compared with one another and then with the evidence bullets from the victims' bodies. Several patterns of striae were observed which displayed remarkable agreement and confirmed that the Dan Wesson revolver was the murder weapon (see Figs. 32 & 33).

The confession of Jeff Turner set the stage for the introduction of the bolt cutters and the Dan Wesson revolver identification. At trial, the defendants were convicted and sent to State Prison. About twelve years later, the crime laboratory analyst was re-subpoenaed to testify in a new sentencing hearing as the result of an appeal. Such a hearing is like a mini-trial and is costly to the State was well as all the participants. The appeal of original sentence was filed for Scott Hammer. He was again sentenced to life. A short time prior to this writing, the State Attorney's office advised that another appeal had been filed for Scott Hammer, on a new technicality, and it was likely that the evidence would have to be presented again. As far as known, that action is still pending.

*Fig. 32 – Revolver recovered from pond

*Fig. 33 – Fatal bullet comparison; evidence left of divider,
test bullet to right of dividing line.

"ONCE A COP..."

I

The Serial Number Problem

The old saying "once a cop, always a cop" was brought home on a case often thought of as "my favorite identification". A simple follow through on an investigative opportunity became a conclusive link in a circumstantial chain of evidence in the murder of a state police officer. This is how it happened.

One business day, the Chief Clerk of the Registration and Gun Files Section of the State Police Record Bureau called the laboratory. He advised he had a client, Edward Brewer, who had brought in an old model .38 special caliber Colt revolver with a possibly altered serial number and requested a check to make sure the firearm was legal. Michigan, like many states, has strict laws governing the reliability of firearm serial numbers. Possession of a firearm, especially a concealed handgun, with an altered serial number, is a serious offense. The Clerk sent Mr. Brewer upstairs to the Crime Laboratory so that a firearms examiner could check the questioned number. Ed Brewer was turned over to me and I examined his old Colt. The primary serial number appeared somewhat indistinct and difficult to read. It looked like an over-stamp with a ghost-like or halo image. A quick check of a hidden serial number disclosed that the primary number was correct and there was no evidence of intentional alteration.

While all this was occurring, Mr. Brewer confided that he had spent much of his adult life in state prison for a variety of offenses, but that he had gone straight for several years. That's why he brought the gun in as soon as he noticed the possible problem. He didn't want any trouble with the law again. After purchasing the revolver from a pawn shop dealer, he took instant action to insure it was legal. As Ed related his story, he was asked if it would be permissible to fire his Colt to obtain tests for routine checking. He stated "That's fine with me, anything to be helpful." Several test shots were fired and the bullets and cartridges cases obtained, preserved, marked for identification and placed in marked and sealed coin envelopes. The tests were then placed in the yearly marked test shot box and secured in the evidence room. The revolver was returned to Mr. Brewer and he left the headquarters building.

The Murder

About a year later, Trooper Ray Barlow was abruptly awakened by a persistent knocking on his apartment door. The young officer lived in an apartment complex just inside the city limits and he had gone to bed early to be fresh for an early assignment the next day. He got up, threw on a bathrobe, and went to the door. He was met by the manager of the apartments, who had become a friend to the young officer. The manager was obviously quite agitated and advised the trooper that there was some type of disturbance in another part of the complex, possibly a family fight, and he thought he might need some assistance. Ray grabbed his badge and snub-nose revolver and stuck them in his bathrobe pocket. He put on his slippers quickly and followed the manager.

What the manager and Tpr. Barlow didn't know was that the reported disturbance was not a family fight. Instead, it was the result of an armed drug robbery. As the officer and manager rounded the hallway corner of the indicated apartment section, they were abruptly met by two individuals with drawn handguns. Before the trooper could get his hand and revolver out of the bathrobe pocket, one of the men fired his revolver striking the officer, creating a fatal wound.

The two strangers brushed the manager aside, fled the apartment building, and made good their escape.

The crime scene was inside the city limits of Detroit and the City Police Department and Wayne County Medical Examiner had jurisdiction and took charge of the investigation. The fatal bullet was removed at autopsy by the M.E. and turned over to the city crime laboratory where it was examined by forensic firearms analysts. In short order, the laboratory advised the bullet was .38 special caliber and displayed class rifling characteristics of six lands and grooves, with a left hand twist, and with land and groove impression widths of about .058/.122". As is generally known in police and forensic circles, class characteristics of fired bullets can be compared with known specimens and data from firearms examined and measured throughout many parts of the world. In this case, the rifling data "matched" several revolvers, but of that short list the more likely firearm was that of a Colt revolver.

The Forensic Connection

Of course, the entire state police organization was shocked and angered by the senseless killing of the young trooper. A team of detectives was assigned to work with the city officers to assist in developing and running down leads.

Early in the investigation, two senior State Police detectives came into the crime laboratory one morning and asked to talk to the author. They reported they had been following a lead on two potential suspects, known criminals with extensive records, including armed robbery. These two individuals had been paroled from State Prison recently. They stated that they learned the two had stayed for a short time with an old ex-con, located in a suburb of Detroit. They said further that the old timer was named Ed Brewer, and they had just completed interviewing him.

Ed Brewer told them that the two possible suspects left his place shortly after the killing. They stated they asked Ed if the suspects had any firearms with them and he said he hadn't seen any. They then inquired whether or not Ed had any guns, and he advised that he had an old model Colt revolver, .38 special caliber, and that he kept it in a dresser drawer. Of course, they asked if they could see the revolver. When Ed checked the drawer, it wasn't there. A complete search of the house failed to turn up the missing handgun, and it was never seen again. Ed Brewer then volunteered the information to the officers that if they needed more information on his gun they should go to State Police Headquarters and talk to the firearms guy in the crime laboratory. He told them the story of the possibly altered serial number and, even more importantly, that the revolver had been routinely test fired while it was in the laboratory!

The officers asked whether or not I could recall such an incident with Ed Brewer. Of course, that was easy, although it was a routine matter, it was somewhat unusual. The test shots from Ed's Colt revolver were retrieved from the evidence room and turned over to the detectives. The specimens were then immediately taken to the Detroit Crime Laboratory where they were identified as having been fired from the same barrel as the fatal bullet from Tpr. Barlow.

Not long after, the two suspects were apprehended in another city and returned to Wayne County to stand trial for murder. The Colt firearm was never recovered, but the information from Ed Brewer and the bullet identification materially assisted in the conviction of the killers.

Even though the vital bullet identification was done elsewhere, the link to the test specimens provided a great deal of satisfaction. This case illustrated once more that being a successful analyst in the crime laboratory requires more than analytical and comparative skills. The examiner must be willing and able to look beyond the requested or routine examination and seek out other possibly related evidence links.

MERRY CHRISTMAS FROM THE SYNAGOGUE KILLER

I

The Murder

Late at night, Myron Hinkley was making his final rounds. Being night watchman at a famous Synagogue wasn't what you might call exciting. However, it was clean, respectful, and the silent atmosphere didn't seem to bother Myron. But now he was investigating a faint unusual noise, which seemed to emerge from the rear of the ground floor area, near the vault. As he approached the vicinity, he may have thought he only imagined the sound. He turned down the corridor toward the area and the lights literally went out. An upraised crowbar descended quickly, partially crushing his skull, rendering him unconscious and very soon dead.

Myron could not have known that a pair of professional burglars had entered the Synagogue and broken through the concrete wall of the vault. Apparently one of the pair had seen or heard him coming and made a decision to kill him rather than be caught. This particular duo specialized in vault break-ins, the type of MO or method of operation that often produced large amounts of money or valuables. This Synagogue was arguably the best known in the state and the property and buildings would indicate a comparatively wealthy congregation.

The crime was discovered within a few hours and the local police department notified. The area was secured and protected for processing of the crime scene. The local department was fortunate to have, as an Identification Officer, a graduate of Michigan State University's forensic science program, Robert Blackmer. Bob had worked closely with the State Crime Laboratory on several cases and it was common knowledge that he was a model for proper handling, and marking of evidence submitted to the laboratory. Naturally this made him quite popular with the analysts.

Bob and his associate spent many hours at the vault area searching for physical evidence that might be tied to the culprits. They were disappointed at every turn. There were no foreign identifiable fingerprints detected, and no significant trace material such as foreign hair or fibers. However, careful sorting of documents, carelessly swept onto the floor, disclosed an 8x11" sheet of white correspondence paper. Very careful examination revealed a faint partial shoe/heel impression in dust on the paper. Later, Bob described the imprint when it was brought to the crime laboratory, "It's not much, but it's all the physical evidence we've got."

In the Crime Laboratory

Several weeks after the murder of the night watchman, Bob Blackmer came into the crime laboratory and requested assistance. He stated that although his department had not been optimistic about solving the Synagogue murder with no suspects and little evidence, they had received a lucky break in the case. Another suburban police department, responding to a silent alarm, had captured two men in the process of breaking into a concrete vault. That agency, being aware of the murder case, had notified Bob about case similarities.

In reviewing the second vault robbery, it was noted that the burglars had knocked a hole in the vault wall of nearly the exact size and location of the Synagogue vault. The method of operation, not far apart in time and distance, was too promising for mere coincidence. A check of the effects of the suspects, including their car and contents, disclosed no link to the murder. However, one of the suspects, Ed Tardiff, was wearing a pair of black dress shoes with a heel pattern similar to the dust imprint on paper retrieved from the Synagogue. Bob produced the evidence sheet of paper, carefully flattened in the bottom of a box so as not to be disturbed or handled, and now a pair of black shoes. He requested a comparison between the imprint and the shoes.

In the beginning, a preliminary examination of the imprint revealed it to be incomplete and very faint. Bob was advised, at that time, that it did not appear promising for an identification or elimination of the shoes due to the faint detail. It was also noted that the heel pattern, found on the sheet of paper, was from a relatively common brand of shoe.

The dust print was examined in several different ways in attempting to enhance the detail. It was subjected to angled and grazing incandescent light, to ultra-violet illumination, and infrared photography without any real success. Finally an old document examiners' trick was employed with some success. The paper was placed at an angle next to a laboratory window that was illuminated with North daylight. In this way, wear and damage detail was more pronounced and the effect was photographed for comparison.

In the "toolmark" produced by footwear such as Ed Tardiff's, an examiner must find worn, damaged and/or cut surface areas in the imprint of the heel, or possibly artifacts such as nails, bits of glass or metal, stones, etc., which produce defects in the impression. The molds used to manufacture the heels may be used to manufacture large numbers of such heels and the pattern or manufacturing defects only limit the sample size but don't allow for individualization. It was immediately obvious which heel was the guilty party, if in fact these shoes were involved. The heel of choice was examined visually by aid of the stereo microscope, photographed, test imprints made and also photographed for comparison purposes.

The heel imprint, although faint, displayed a pattern and size similar to the suspected heel. Fortunately, the heel was sufficiently worn so that the pattern displayed irregular worn and broken areas, providing random individual peculiarities.

As the examination progressed, the analyst slowly but surely recognized that there were numerous similarities between the heel and the dust imprint on paper. He finally came to the inescapable conclusion that this heel caused the dust imprint at the murder scene. He called his friend, Bob Blackmer, to advise him that he had been mistaken in his original appraisal of the evidence and that he was reporting a positive identification. (See Figs. 34 & 35).

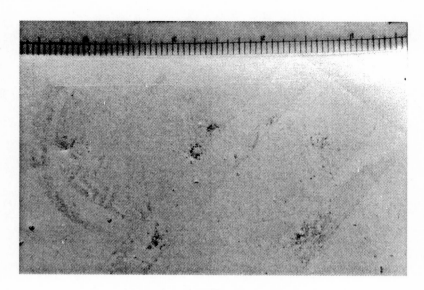

*Fig. 34 – Heel print in dust on synagogue paper.

*Fig. 35 – Defendant's shoe heel (in reverse).

Court and Christmas

Later, at the District Court examination of Ed Tardiff on a murder charge, the laboratory analyst had just been excused from the stand. A recess was called, by the judge, and the defendant asked the court officers if he could speak to the analyst. The officers started to hustle him away, but the laboratory examiner advised them it was okay, he didn't mind if the defendant spoke to him. It might be well to hear what he had to say.

Ed first congratulated the analyst on his expert professional testimony and then stated, "Okay, you've got me convinced, my shoes were there, but I wasn't wearing them!" It might be noted that there was insufficient evidence to charge his partner with the Synagogue murder, and Ed never would talk about the case to the investigators.

In Circuit Court, based on the method of operation, availability timeline, and the shoe identification, Ed was convicted of felony murder and was sentenced to life in prison. He was transferred to the country's largest walled prison, State Prison of Southern Michigan. For several years, the crime lab examiner received a Christmas card every year until he retired and moved. The first card is pictured next (Fig. 36). Such recognition makes one wonder sometimes!

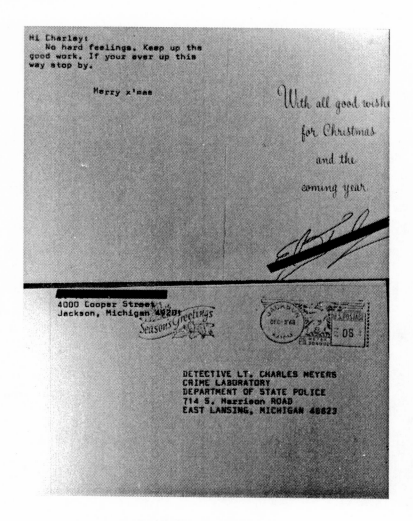

*Fig. 36 – Xmas card from the defendant.

THE NURSE AND THE NYLON—66

I

The Proposition

In the small home, in an older section of town, Todd and Virginia
Gilmore were preparing for the day's work. Todd had an early
shift at a local factory and as usual was on the run, grabbing some
peanut butter toast, and out the door. His wife, Virginia, a nurse at
the local hospital, began work an hour later and was in no hurry. She
had put on her uniform and was preparing a simple breakfast, when
she heard the front doorbell ring. She wondered who that could be
at this early hour, and was surprised to find a strange young man on
the porch when she opened the door. Robert McElvoy identified
himself as a neighbor and stated he needed some urgent medical
advice concerning his mother. Virginia let him in.

What Virginia didn't know was that Robert, who lived a few
blocks away, had noticed her some time before. Virginia was young,
very attractive and cut a nice figure in her nurse's uniform. Robert
had dreamed and fantasized of sex with her. He had always thought
of himself as rather nice looking and attractive to the opposite sex.

After gaining entrance to the home and professing his hastily
made-up story, he finally pulled himself together, confided to her
that he had admired her from afar, and alluded to the real reason
he was there. He bragged that he had been observing her and

her movements for weeks so that he could approach her after her husband had left for work. He confided that he was prepared to turn her humdrum existence into one of rapture and fulfillment through his sexual prowess.

At that, Virginia made a fatal mistake. Believing him to be a relatively harmless teenager with run away sexual fantasies, she laughed at him and told the "little jerk" to get out of her house. Robert picked up a heavy ashtray from a nearby table and struck her a vicious blow to the forehead, shattering the ashtray in the process. Virginia fell to the floor, either unconscious or at least completely dazed. Now Robert was frightened. He knew the assault on the nurse would get him in a lot of trouble. He had to shut her up.

McElvoy's car was parked a short distance away on the opposite side of the street. He ran there quickly, opened the trunk and took a .22 caliber rifle out of the recess, and then ran back to the house. As Virginia was trying to recover, he re-entered the home and placed one well-aimed shot to her head. He then fled the scene, returned home and replaced the rifle in his parent's coat closet.

II

"Forensic Ballistics" at Work

In the Firearms Identification Section of the State Crime Laboratory, a priority examination was ordered for the .22 caliber bullet removed from nurse Gilmore and the fired cartridge case found on the kitchen floor. The examiner first examined the bullet under the stereo microscope for any trace evidence that might be significant, e.g., paint, wood, cement, glass, etc. There were only traces of blood, tissue, bone fragments, etc. Next the bullet was weighed, diameter was calculated, manufacture markings were noted, and the rifling was measured and classified. It was noted that the bullet and fired cartridge case were in agreement as to manufacture. The bullet was found to be a .22 long rifle caliber, lead round nose style, with a remaining weight of 34.2 grains, indicating nearly 6 grains were left in the victim's body. The base displayed a "spindle" mark that was associated with a production line of Remington ammunition. The bullet sides exhibited remnants of six land and groove engraving with a right-hand twist and measurements of @ .022" land impression, and .090" groove impression. It appeared that there were sufficient striae (parallel surface contours created by barrel imperfections visualized as fine lines) to allow for identification of the firearm used in the homicide.

Next, the examiner checked the fired cartridge case from the crime scene. It displayed a typical Remington head-stamp (U), a few granules of flake gunpowder inside the case, a narrow rectangular firing pin impression on the head rim of the case of @.03" in width, an extractor at 3 o'clock and an ejector at about 9 o'clock, and slight concentric breech face markings on the case head. (Markings of a firearm on a cartridge case head are typically located in reference to a clock face position.) These class or family characteristics were found in data and known fired samples from a fairly large number of firearms, made by several different companies. However, in addition, this evidence cartridge case also displayed a number of small impressed marks that appeared like a box shaped series of dots or periods. The style and location suggested a cut out area of the breech face of the firearm to accommodate the ejector mechanism. At this time, in the rather extensive State known fired reference files, there was only one series of tests that met all these criteria. They were test standards from a .22 long rifle caliber Remington semi-automatic rifle, model Nylon-66.

At the time of this murder, this rifle had been on the commercial market for only a year or two. It was a very popular firearm, light in weight, not too expensive, and was called the Nylon-66 due to its innovative plastic stock. Investigating officers were told, although there were a number of firearm possibilities from several different manufacturers, the Remington Nylon-66 rifle was the likely candidate for the murder weapon. They were also advised that the examiner believed there was a good possibility the firearm involved could be positively identified, if it were located and submitted to the laboratory.

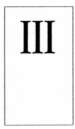

III

The Search

For a brief period, the investigation followed a typical track; neighborhood canvas, interviews with friends, business associates, family members, check of known sexual deviates in the area, parolees, etc., with no real suspects. The detectives decided the firearm relationship might be their only hope and officers followed assigned paths in an ever-widening search of the area for a firearm of the reported type. The crime scene was the hub of the search and searchers spread out as spokes of a wheel. Members of each home along the way were asked if anyone they knew possessed such a firearm.

After a few days, they struck pay-dirt, or so they thought. One family affirmatively responded to their query and produced a .22 LR caliber Remington Nylon-66 rifle. In the household there was a teenager who had access to the firearm. The rifle was rushed to the crime laboratory and immediately examined. Their hopes were dashed as the examiner advised them that the rifle displayed the right class characteristics but the wrong individual characteristics. It was not the firearm involved.

Again, after a few more days of searching, another possible was discovered. The McElvoy household was interviewed and the parents readily admitted that the father owned a Remington Nylon-66. It was produced from a coat closet and turned-over to the detectives. It was taken to the crime lab requesting a "rush".

Again, an immediate examination of this rifle was performed. But this time, everything changed. Both the evidence bullet and fired cartridge case were compared to tests from the rifle, using the conventional comparison microscopic technique of isolating individual characteristics on evidence and test so that they can be viewed side-by-side, under magnification. In this comparison, the examiner found sufficient agreement in both the impressed markings on the cartridge case and striated markings on the bullet to conclude this was the murder weapon!

The officers quickly concluded that Robert McElvoy, the son, was the more logical suspect. After a short interrogation, he admitted responsibility for Virginia Gilmore's murder. However, as is usually the case, he asserted it wasn't all his fault. He told how it all happened and how the beautiful nurse laughed in his face. He said he became so enraged that without thinking he struck her with the ashtray, inflicting a severe cut to her forehead and rendering her unconscious. But then he knew he was in serious trouble and she would have him arrested. He told the officers "don't you see, I was frightened and I had to keep her from talking. I couldn't help myself!"

Of course, a case like this is doubly satisfying to the crime laboratory analyst who provides the key to unlock the door leading to the crime solution.

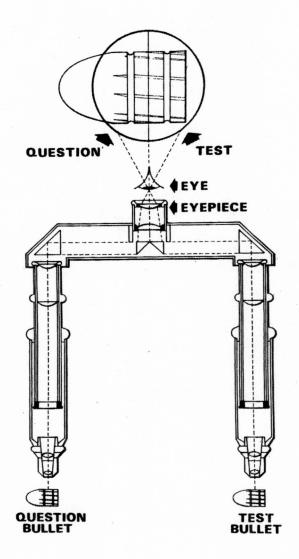

QUESTION   TEST

◀ EYE

◀ EYEPIECE

QUESTION
BULLET

TEST
BULLET

courtesy of A. Biasotti

ADDENDUM

A Primer on Firearms and Toolmark Identification

The following monograph embraces the history and theory of this forensic discipline. It includes important references for anyone seeking further study. (1)

INTRODUCTION

FIREARMS IDENTIFICATION is a discipline of forensic Science directed to the examination and comparative analysis of firearms and ammunition components, with a primary purpose of determining whether, or not, a bullet or cartridge case, was fired by a particular firearm. It may include determination of function and operating condition of firearms, the measurement of class characteristics and comparison with laboratory files to determine type and possible brand name of the firearm used in a crime, bullet flight paths and trajectories, and gunpowder/shot pattern analysis to determine distance of discharge.

Firearms Identification is sometimes referred to as ballistics or forensic ballistics. Ballistics, the study of the motion of a projectile, is subdivided into several areas, originally interior, exterior, and terminal ballistics. Some authorities now include wound and forensic ballistics under this heading. To be precise, ballistics is primarily concerned with velocities, pressure curves, trajectories, in their pure form and not how they relate to firearms identification. Firearms identification and ballistics are not the same thing but they are directly related in that the markings produced on the bullet and cartridge case, the flight path of the projectile, and distance determination based on gunpowder/shot pattern analysis are to some degree dependent on the interior, exterior, terminal, and wound ballistics involved. Firearms Identification attempts to apply ballistic principles to a variety of firearms related problems and relate the evaluation of these problems to the courts. Forensic Ballistics, a term sometimes frowned upon by practitioners, is a combination term which can be defined as the application of ballistics to the purposes of the law (2).

TOOLMARK IDENTIFICATION is based on the principle that when any two objects come in forceful contact with each other, the softer material is often marked with individual characteristics of the harder material. The harder object or instrument is usually referred to as the "tool", and many times actual tools are employed. However, many objects other than tools leave their individual signature on various surfaces. As an example, markings from the bore of a firearm on the sides of a bullet are a specialized form of toolmark.

Toolmarks are generally thought of as two types: *Impressed markings*, sometimes called compression marks, are the result of a crushing type of force. Negative images of the defects on a tool's surface may provide identification of the instrument. *Striated markings*, sometimes called *abrasion or friction markings*, are the result of a tool slipping or being drawn along the surface, creating microscopic valleys and ridges. These markings may be sufficient for identification individualization of the tool.

The markings useful in firearms and toolmark identification are usually compared by use of the <u>forensic comparison microscope</u>. This microscope is basically two compound microscopes of relatively low power, linked together by an optical bridge which allows the viewer to see two magnified objects (i.e., evidence and test bullet) side-by-side, separated by what is referred to as a hairline divider. In this way, individual markings and patterns can be compared for similarity or lack of same.

Most practitioners in firearms and toolmark identification agree that considerable training and supervised casework in the latter stages of training are a pre-requisite for expertise in this forensic discipline. The length of training, usually accomplished in an on-the-job apprentice relationship, may vary somewhat with the amount of advanced "forensic science" oriented education completed and/or work experience in a directly related occupation, such as prior crime laboratory assignments, firearms, ammunition, tool industries, criminal investigation, or positions with diverse scientific or laboratory related responsibilities.

The value of college education is stressed today. Degrees that relate directly to the various crime laboratory disciplines, such as forensic science or criminalistics, physical or natural science, and law enforcement with an emphasis on police science or criminalistics, are usually required. However, there are currently no college programs that will completely educate and/or train an individual to perform these analyses in an acceptably competent manner.

An overview of recommended training may be obtained by reviewing training outlines of large crime laboratories (city, state, or federal) and regional forensic science associations. In addition, the Association of Firearm and Tool Mark Examiners (AFTE) has published a Glossary and Training Manual to assist practitioners in training in this important area (3,4). Such training sources are also invaluable for their bibliographies.

In addition to educational requirements, some insight into personal traits and training requirements in this discipline should be considered by noting those formulated by the original AFTE Peer Group on Certification (circa 1979) that included the following <u>minimum</u> standards:

> "...must be of good moral character, high integrity, good repute, and professional standing...
>
> ...be required to document a minimum of a full time one year laboratory training program or it's equivalent... such training shall be directly related to firearms and/or toolmark identification...
>
> ...must document one year full time supervised laboratory experience or its equivalent in the practice of firearms and toolmark identification..."

DEVELOPMENT

"Striation matching" is the cornerstone upon which most microscopic comparisons in this field depend. At the outset, striations or stria (pl. striae) are defined as minute grooves or channels; threadlike lines or narrow bands, especially when occurring as a series of parallel lines.

A number of famous scientists from about 1900 pointed out the legal or forensic significance of these markings in a number of situations involving firearms and toolmark identification. Some authorities credit Dr. R. Kockel of the Institute of Legal Medicine, University of Leipzig, with demonstrating the use of striation matching of toolmarks in several papers published circa 1900 – 1905 (5). In his first classic papers, Kockel pointed out the identification of a knife with cuts in wood, "where small trees along the street had been damaged by crude people." He described methods for producing test marks with the knife and for using oblique lighting, and measurement of relative spacing by vernier calipers. The article included illustrations of these identifications. It is also interesting to note that he mentioned the changing spatial relationship of tool markings with changed angles of the blade.

Prof. Reiss of Lausanne described the method in 1911 and Balthazard and later DeRechter explained the technique in some detail during the period of 1912 – 1929. Forensic Science is indebted to Dr. Thomas of the University of Ghent for a 1947 paper dealing with toolmarks in a skull and for a 1967 paper where he brought together much of the historical references on striation matching. Dr. Thomas reported on the identification of an axe with defects in the victim's skull, using the method of DeRechter. The article is illustrated with matching photographs of evidence and test markings, followed by an explanation of the mathematical probability developed (6).

Over the years, many forensic scientists have reported the use of myriads of toolmarks, in many types of case solutions. The ranks of these experts, to name but a few, include David Burd and Roger

Greene of California, Emmet Flynn and Art Paholke of Chicago, and Wolfgang Bonte of Germany (7,8). John Davis, of California, must be mentioned for his many contributions and his text on "Toolmarks, Firearms, and the Striagraph" (9).

In firearms identification, important references appear earlier than 1900 and continue to this day. Most early attempts involved determination of shape, caliber and type of projectile along with gross imperfections imprinted on the surface of a bullet or cartridge case (10). In 1835, a London policeman matched a bullet to a defect in the bullet mould of the suspect. In the 1860s, Civil War shootings were reportedly solved by comparison of shape and caliber of fatal bullets. In 1900, Dr. Albert Hall wrote in some detail on land and groove impression measurements (11). Balthazard, a physician and civil engineer, published classical papers in the early 1900s on a method of comparing bullets and cartridge cases with enlarged photographs (12).

The most important set of circumstances, at least in this hemisphere, began with the developments in the Stielow case. Charlie Stielow had been convicted of first degree murder and was sentenced to death. The primary evidence against him at the trial in 1915 was the testimony of a "firearms expert" who stated the fatal bullets were fired from Stielow's .22 caliber revolver. C. E. Waite, an investigator with the New York Attorney General's office, along with others, principally Dr. Max Poser of Bausch & Lomb, proved that Stielow's firearm was not involved. This led Waite to seek information on firearms and cartridges and ultimately to form a group of individuals to conduct research and examinations in "forensic ballistics" as it later became known. The group consisted of Waite, Phillip O. Gravelle, a microscopist and photographer, John H. Fisher, a tool designer, and Calvin H. Goddard, a medical doctor and ordnance officer. The primary element was Goddard, who is recognized by many as the "father of modern firearms identification." They were instrumental in adapting the comparison microscope to firearms identification, including the use of special stages and bullet mounting devices developed by Remington Corp., and for the helixometer, a device used to examine barrel bores and measure rifling pitch. In 1925 in New York, they were known as the Bureau of Forensic Ballistics. Today they are thought of as one of the major factors in the development of forensic science and the crime laboratory. The infamous Valentine Day Massacre in Chicago in 1929 is credited with bringing Goddard to Chicago to establish the Scientific Crime Laboratory in affiliation with Northwestern University in 1930 (13).

The list of contributors to the literature of firearms identification is lengthy. One expert of note is Maj. General Julian S. Hatcher, whose "Texbook of Firearms Investigation, Identification, and Evidence" is considered to be the hallmark text on the subject by many in this field (14). Another pioneer was Charles O. Gunther, who along with his brother J. D. Gunther, authored the most detailed material on comparison aspects of the science and legal cases of note in "Firearms Identification" (15). J. Howard Mathews must be mentioned for his monumental research work in three volumes, "Firearms Identification", with assists from several others, including Ralph Turner and Al Wilimovsky (16). Some other major contributors would include Dr. Wilfred Derome of Quebec (17), Sir Gerald Burrard (18). Sir Sydney Smith, Robert Churchill, and Major Hugh Pollard of England, and, in recent years, Al Biasotti of California (19).

Mention must be made of a group of individuals responsible for the development and growth of the Association of Firearm and Tool Mark Examiners (AFTE). In 1969, with the encouragement of the Chicago Police Department Crime Laboratory, a group of interested parties met in Chicago and formed AFTE. The main elements of this beginning were John Stauffer of the Chicago Police Department, Burton Munhall of Federal Cartridge Corp., and Walter Howe. The idea was to bring together as many individuals, as possible, who were active in some aspect of firearms identification to share their knowledge and methods for the benefit of all.

The organizing force and prime mover of this new organization was Howe. Walter J. Howe, gunsmith, author, firearms expert, editor of the American Rifleman, and later Vice-President of Sturm, Roger Corp., pushed those of us fortunate enough to be near him into a viable organization. He was the first President of AFTE and publisher of its Newsletter, later to become the AFTE Journal. This association is currently one of the more successful forensic groups and has brought forth more information on the subject of firearms and toolmarks than ever assembled in one place. AFTE has become international in scope with members from all over the globe. Mention of this important group would not be complete without acknowledgement of the late Steve Molnar of the Ohio Bureau of Criminal Identification Laboratory. For many years, he authored numerous articles and published the Newsletter and the Journal for AFTE.

In recent years, one of the major developments in criminalistics or police science has been the efforts of the Federal Bureau of Investigation and its laboratory arm with the Forensic Science and Research group to assist in the training of crime laboratory analysts in various disciplines. The FBI Laboratory has been known for the quality of its training programs, and through courses such as "Gunshot and Primer Residue" and "Specialized Techniques in Firearms Identification," they are assisting city, state, and other federal crime laboratories. In addition, they have assembled known specimens and data bases to assist all in the discipline.

IDENTIFICATION/INDIVIDUALIZATION THEORY AND CRITERIA FOR IDENTIFICATION

With few exceptions, the action surfaces of firearms are composed of cast, forged, or stamped metal alloys. Those surfaces in a firearm which directly support the cartridge and projectile are, of necessity, tool worked or engraved to provide smooth finishes and close tolerances. Such surfaces would include the breechblock, boltface, and chamber, which support the cartridge at discharge and the barrel bore which supports the projectile during the early milli-seconds of its movement.

Various parts of the mechanism also have intimate contact with the cartridge case and the projectile. Such parts include the firing pin or striker, the extractor, ejector, magazine, feed ramp, forcing cone, lead to the rifling, etc. The sequence of manufacturing and tool working of these surfaces, along with later use and abuse, is of prime importance in that the defects vital to the identification process arise from these actions. The combination of cutting/tearing and/or displacement of the metal, caused during manufacture, and the further changes in the surfaces from use, corrosion, and erosion, provide a number and variety of surface irregularities, pits, protrusions, ridges, valleys, troughs, etc. These defects may be impressed upon or produce striations upon the corresponding contact surfaces of the cartridge case or bullet. It should also be remembered that such toolmarks are produced under the influence of expansion and upset caused by breech pressures on the order of 10,000 – 50,000 lbs./sq./inch, depending on the firearm and cartridge combination.

As mentioned earlier, the technique usually involved is that of the classical comparison using the forensic comparison microscope. At least two test fired bullets and cartridge cases are obtained from the suspected firearm. Typically the tests are compared with each other to assess the available patterns of markings and their replication. They are then compared with the evidence exhibits of similar class.

It is the combination of such patterns, impressed and/or striated, which allows bullets and cartridge cases to be compared and identified as having been fired by a particular weapon. A Sub-Committee of AFTE attempted to describe this process in a cogent manner (20).

"The theory of identification as it pertains to the comparison of toolmarks enables opinions of common origin to be made when the unique surface contours of two toolmarks are in sufficient agreement.

This sufficient agreement is related to the significant duplication of random toolmarks as evidence by the correspondence of a pattern or combination of patterns of surface contours.

Significance is determined by the comparative examination of two or more sets of surface contour patterns comprised of individual peaks, ridges, and furrows. Specifically, the relative height or depth, width, curvature, and spatial relationship of the individual peaks, ridges, and furrows within one set of surface contours are defined and compared to the corresponding features in the second set of surface contours. Agreement is significant when it exceeds the best agreement demonstrated between toolmarks known to have been produced by different tools and is consistent with the agreement demonstrated by toolmarks, known to have been, produced by the same tool. The statement that sufficient agreement exists between the two tool marks means that the likelihood another tool could have made the mark is so remote as to be considered a practical impossibility. Currently the interpretation of individualization/identification is subjective in nature, founded on scientific principles, and based on the examiner's training and experience."

An evaluation of the foregoing quote reveals several points for consideration. In the first instance, it is not the individual surface contour that can be determined as unique, rather the pattern or groups of such contours that can be unique to a certain firearm or tool. When toolmarks are said to exceed the best agreement of known non-matches, it is really a statement that they exceed to a considerable degree the agreement seen in non-matches. Lastly, supervised training and experience in examining and evaluating literally hundreds, if not thousands, of known matches and non-matches are required to develop the mental inventory and comparative judgment required in this work.

John Thornton described it well: "This process of examination of known weapons and projectiles may in the case of a new firearms examiner be repeated for scores of cycles before the examiner begins to forge a notion of uniqueness in the smithy of his own consciousness" (21). Biasotti, also emphasized "the objective standards used are developed by each practitioner through practical experience, using the scientific method of problem solving: Observe, record, analyze, and hypothesize" (22).

It has been pointed out that this process is both objective and subjective in nature, with objective standards and materials being used as a backdrop for the subjective opinion relying on the examiner's "…knowledge, perception, reason, and interpretation" (23).

RECENT DEVELOPMENTS

In the 80s and 90s there has been continuous and expanding research in the discipline, with special emphasis on objective criteria for identification. This effort had been of even greater importance very recently due to the impact of the Supreme Court decision in "Daubert v. Merrell Dow Pharmaceuticals, Co." (509 US579, 1993), relating to a scientific validity test for the admission of physical evidence opinion testimony.

A number of discipline experts have been very active in this research effort. One "unsung hero", who has been responsible for important communications and technical papers in this regard, is Tsuneo Uchiyama of Japan (24). Efforts in the United States have been assisted by cooperation of a number of city, state, and federal agencies, including the Federal Bureau of Investigation Forensic Research and Training group. The efforts have been spurred on by the development of improved electronic scanning apparatus and automated comparison systems.

Chief among the United States practitioners, who have led in this research effort, were Al Biasotti (recently deceased) and John Murdock of California. They have co-authored a chapter on Firearms and Toolmarks Identification, with material dealing with the concept of scientific validity and including historical and up-to-date information on the discipline, with an emphasis on theory of identification and objective/quantified criteria. All serious students and practitioners should thoroughly read and review this material, published as part of "Modern Scientific Evidence – The Law and Science of Expert Testimony," by West (25).

Most recently, Ronald G. Nichols published a compendium of modern articles and papers that deal to a great degree with the basis for firearms and toolmark identification (26). Many are "empirical studies," or what some older practitioners called "applied research," but they help form the matrix for the discipline's "criteria for identification." This contribution, along with the cited papers should be required reading.

REFERENCES

(1)   Meyers, C., "Firearms and Toolmark Identification – An introduction, *"Journal of the Association of Firearm and Tool Mark Examiners (AFTE),* Vol. 25, No. 4, Oct. 93, 281 – 285.

(2)   Barnes, F. C., *Cartridges of the World*, 4th. Ed., DBI Books, Inc,, Northfield, Il 1980.

(3)   *Glossary of the Association of Firearm and Tool Mark Examiners,* Fonville Printing Co., Augusta, Ga. 1980.

(4)   *Training Manual of the Association of Firearm and Tol Mark Examiners*, AFTE, 1982.

(5)   Kockel, R., "Ueber die Darstellung der Spuren von Messer-Scharten," and Weitares uber die Identifizierung von Schartenspurten," *Archiv fur Kriminal-Anthropologie und Kriminalistik*, 5 of 1900, and 11 of 1903 (translated/reprinted AFTE Journal Vol. 12, July 1980, 16 – 28).

(6)   Thomas, F., "Comments on the Discovery of Striation Matching and of Early Contributions for Forensic Firearms Identification," *Journal of Forensic Sciences*, Vol. 12, no. 1, Jan 1967, (reprinted AFTE Journal, Vol. 12, July 1980, 31 – 35).

(7)   Burd, D. Q., and Greene, R. S., "Tool Mark Comparisons in Criminal Investigations," *Journal of Criminal Law and Criminology*, Vol. 39, No. 3, Oct. 1948.

(8)   Bonte, W., "Tool Marks in Bones and Cartilage," *Journal of Forensic Sciences*, Vol. 20, No. 2, Apr. 1975.

(9)   Davis, John E., *Tool Marks, Firearms and the Striagraph*, Charles C. Thomas, Springfield, IL. 1958.

(10) Berg, S. O., "The Drama of Forensic Ballistics," *AFTE Journal*, Vol. 11, No. 3, July 1979.

(11) Hall, A. L. "The Missile and the Weapon," *The Buffalo Medical Journal,* June 1900.

(12) Balthazard, V., "Identification de projectiles d'armes a feu," *Archives d'anthropologie criminille,* 28, 1913.

(13) Goddard, C. H., "The Valentine's Day Massacre: A Study in Ammunition Tracing," *American Journal of Police Science,* Vol. 1, No. 1, 1930 (reprinted AFTE Journal, Vol. 12, No. 1, 1980).

(14) Hatcher, J. S., "*Textbook of Firearms Investigation, Identification, and Evidence,*" Samworth, Georgetown, SC, 1935 and 1946.

(15) Gunther, C. O., and Gunther, J. D., "*Firearms Identification,*" John Wiley & Sons, New York, 1935.

(16) Mathews, J. H., "*Firearms Identification,*" Vols. I, II, & III, Charles C. Thomas, Springfield, IL, 1962 – 1973.

(17) Derome, W., "*Expertise on Arms A Feu,*" Canada, 1929.

(18) Burrard, G., "*The Identification of Firearms and Forensic Ballistics,*" Herbert Jenkins, London, 1934, and A. S. Barnes, New York, 1962.

(19) Biasotti, A., "A Statistical Study of the Individual Characteristics of Fired Bullets," *Journal of Forensic Sciences,* Vol. 4, No. 1, 1959.

(20) A Combined Standardization and Criteria Sub-Committee Report, "Theory of Identification as It Relates to Toolmarks," *AFTE Journal,* Vol. 24, No. 3, July 1992, 337.

(21) Thornton, J., "The Validity of Firearms Evidence," *The California Attys. For Criminal Justice: Forum,* Vol. 5, No. 4, Aug. 1978.

(22) Biasotti, A., *"Firearms Identification Based Upon Bullet Comparisns: Expertise or Guess Work?"* An Analysis and Opinion, Sept. 1977.

(23) Meyers, C., "The Objective v. Subjective Boondoggle," *AFTE Journal*, Vol. 19, No. 1, Jan. 1987, 24-30.

(24) Uchiyama, T., "Automated Landmark Identification System," *AFTE Journal*, Vol. 25, 1993, 172.

(25) Faigman, D., et al, Two Volumes, *"Modern Scientific Evidence: The Law and Science of Expert Testimony,"* West Publishing, St. Paul. MN, 1997.

(26) Nichols, R., "Firearm and Toolmark Identification Criteria: A Review of the Literature," *Journal of Forensic Sciences*, 1997; 42 (3): 466-474 and Part II, *Journal of Forensic Sciences*, 2003, 48 (2), 318-327.

POSTSCRIPT

In Forensic Science it is often said "physical evidence does not lie." However, it can be misinterpreted or even worse, distorted. In recent history, the public has been exposed to several "famous forensic scientists" who have testified to speculative opinions as if they were factual, who have testified to issues or matters outside their areas of bona fide training and expertise, or have been mistaken in their conclusions for one reason or another.

How does one explain an "expert" who reportedly identified old toolmarks in cement as possible shoeprints in blood? Or, how about the "criminalist" who changed an obvious murder into a "tragic accident" by establishing a probable bullet trajectory with little or no real basis in fact. It is to be hoped that these were honest mistakes and not related to the sometimes large sums of money available for expert witnesses in certain cases.

It should be pointed out that the vast majority of experts in the firearms and toolmark discipline, as well ass others normally associated with recognized crime laboratories, are dedicated and hard-working public servants who toil willingly for nominal (sometimes mediocre) salaries, and who make a minimum amount of mistakes in the performance of their duties. After nearly fifty years within the system, it is my opinion that the ethics and professionalism of these individuals compares favorably or exceeds those of most of their forensic and legal critics.

Be that as it may, I still recall one of my early homicide trials, where an effective old-time defense attorney asked me, the ancient query for expert witnesses; "Have you ever made a mistake?" I immediately went into a standard reply, which goes something like; "If by that question you are asking whether or not I have ever made a mistaken toolmark identification or elimination, the answer, to the best of my knowledge, is I have not. However, if you are asking whether or not I have ever made a mistake in my lifetime, the answer is certainly yes."

During the recess, the old attorney advised me that, years before he had been cross-examining my old boss, Lt. Leroy Smith, who was the expert witness in a shooting of that time period, that he felt Smitty had a better answer to that query. I, of course, asked what that better answer was and he replied, "It was just one word, yes!"

ACKNOWLEDGEMENTS

A special note of thanks is due my lovely wife, Nancy Meyers, my grandchildren Michael, Joseph, and Thomas McKiernan, Chelsea and Lindsey Meyers, my nephew Jason Loosemore, and my good friend, Rosemary Cross. Without their inspiration and patient help this project may never have been completed.

It is vital to express my appreciation to the literally hundreds of police and crime laboratory professionals with whom I have had the pleasure of working closely for over fifty years. In particular, I must mention the laboratory specialists of the Michigan State Police and Florida Department of Law Enforcement Crime Laboratories.

Finally, I would like to quote from my favorite true crime novel, "The Michigan Murders," by Edward Keyes, "...the Michigan State Police as an organization – tough, uncompromising, one of the proudest and most capable law enforcement agencies I have encountered anywhere..."

Printed in the United States
21407LVS00002B/67-228